D1266589

SONGS
for
JUNIORS

BROADMAN PRESS
Nashville, Tennessee

SONGS FOR JUNIORS

Here is a hymnbook just for Juniors. The title says so, but that is not all. For several years many teachers and other friends of Juniors listened to them sing. Then they helped us make up this selection of hymns and songs that Juniors like to sing. Thousands of Juniors like them because they are singable and meaningful.

Many songs are in this book, and they were written by many different people. But each writer had something in his heart to say to God—to praise him, to thank him for his goodness, to ask for help, to pledge allegiance to his Son. A psalm writer summed it up best: "O sing unto the Lord a new song; for he hath done marvelous things."

Now *you* can use these words and melodies—the favorites of many other Juniors—to sing your own praise and prayer and loyalty. Make the words you sing your own words. Only as you sing out of your heart will you "sing unto the Lord."

THE EDITORS

Copyright 1953, by
BROADMAN PRESS
Nashville, Tennessee

Printed in the United States of America
100KP353.

SONGS *for* JUNIORS

When Morning Gilds the Skies

1

From the German
Translated by EDWARD CASWALL

JOSEPH BARNBY

1. When morn-ing gilds the skies, My heart a-wak-ing cries:
2. Does sad-ness fill my mind, A sol-ace here I find:
3. In heaven's e-ter-nal bliss The love-liest strain is this,
4. Be this, while life is mine, My can-ti-cle di-vine,

May Je-sus Christ be praised! A-like at work and prayer
May Je-sus Christ be praised! Or fades my earth-ly bliss,
May Je-sus Christ be praised! The powers of dark-ness fear,
May Je-sus Christ be praised! Be this th'e-ter-nal song,

To Je-sus I re-pair: May Je-sus Christ be praised!
My com-fort still is this: May Je-sus Christ be praised!
When this sweet chant they hear: May Je-sus Christ be praised!
Through all the a-ges long: May Je-sus Christ be praised!

All Things Bright and Beautiful

Mrs. C. F. Alexander

Adapted from Louis Spohr

1. All things bright and beau-ti - ful, All things great and small,
2. Cold wind in the win - ter, Pleas-ant sum-mer sun,

All things wise and won-der-ful, Our Fa - ther made them all.
Ripe fruits in the gar - den, He made them ev - 'ry one.

Each lit - tle flower that o - pens, Each lit - tle bird that sings,
He gave us eyes to see them, And lips that we might tell

He made their glow-ing col - ors, He made their ti - ny wings.
How good is God our Fa - ther Who do-eth all things well.

Joyful, Joyful, We Adore Thee

HENRY VAN DYKE

Arranged from LUDWIG VON BEETHOVEN

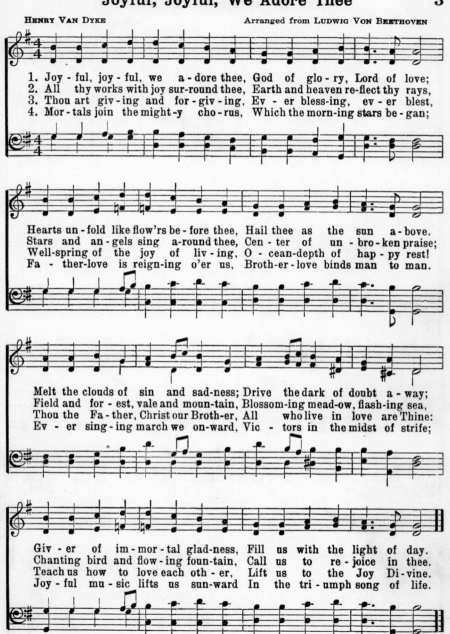

1. Joy - ful, joy - ful, we a - dore thee, God of glo - ry, Lord of love;
2. All thy works with joy sur - round thee, Earth and heaven re - flect thy rays,
3. Thou art giv - ing and for - giv - ing, Ev - er bless - ing, ev - er blest,
4. Mor - tals join the might - y cho - rus, Which the morn - ing stars be - gan;

Hearts un - fold like flow'rs be - fore thee, Hail thee as the sun a - bove.
Stars and an - gels sing a - round thee, Cen - ter of un - bro - ken praise;
Well-spring of the joy of liv - ing, O - cean-depth of hap - py rest!
Fa - ther-love is reign-ing o'er us, Broth-er - love binds man to man.

Melt the clouds of sin and sad-ness; Drive the dark of doubt a - way;
Field and for - est, vale and moun-tain, Blossom-ing mead-ow, flash-ing sea,
Thou the Fa - ther, Christ our Broth-er, All who live in love are Thine:
Ev - er sing-ing march we on-ward, Vic - tors in the midst of strife;

Giv - er of im - mor - tal glad-ness, Fill us with the light of day.
Chanting bird and flow - ing foun-tain, Call us to re - joice in thee.
Teach us how to love each oth - er, Lift us to the Joy Di - vine.
Joy - ful mu - sic lifts us sun-ward In the tri - umph song of life.

Reprinted from The Poems of Henry van Dyke; Copyright 1911 by Charles Scribner's Sons, 1939 by Tertius van Dyke; Used by permission of the publishers

4   Day Is Dying in the West

MARY A. LATHBURY

WILLIAM F. SHERWIN

1. Day is dy-ing in the west, Heaven is touching earth with rest; Wait and
2. Lord of life, be-neath the dome Of the u-ni-verse, Thy home, Gath-er
3. While the deepening shadows fall, Heart of Love, en-fold-ing all, Thro' the
4. When for-ev-er from our sight Pass the stars, the day, the night, Lord of

wor-ship while the night Sets her evening lamps alight Thro' all the sky.
us, who seek Thy face, To the fold of Thy embrace, For Thou art nigh.
glo-ry and the grace Of the stars that veil Thy face, Our hearts as-cend.
an-gels, on our eyes Let e-ter-nal morn-ing rise, And shad-ows end!

REFRAIN

Ho-ly, Ho-ly, Ho-ly, Lord God of Hosts! Heaven and earth are

full of Thee! Heaven and earth are prais-ing Thee, O Lord Most High!

Battle Hymn of the Republic

Julia Ward Howe

Plantation Melody

1. Mine eyes have seen the glo-ry of the com-ing of the Lord; He is
2. I have seen Him in the watchfires of a hun-dred circling camps; They have
3. He has sounded forth the trumpet that shall nev-er sound re-treat; He is
4. In the beau-ty of the lil-ies, Christ was born a-cross the sea, With a

trampling out the vintage where the grapes of wrath are stored; He hath loosed the
build - ed Him an al - tar in the evening dews and damps; I can read His
sift - ing out the hearts of men be-fore His judg-ment seat. O be swift, my
glo - ry in His bos - om that trans-fig-ures you and me; As He died to

fate-ful light'ning of His ter - ri-ble swift sword; His truth is march-ing on.
righteous sentence by the dim and flaring lamps; His day is march-ing on.
soul, to ans-wer Him! be ju - bi-lant my feet! Our God is march-ing on.
make men ho-ly, let us die to make men free; While God is marching on.

CHORUS

Glo-ry! glo-ry, hal-le-lu - jah! Glo-ry! glo-ry, hal-le-lu - jah!

Glo-ry! glo-ry, hal-le-lu - jah! Our God is march-ing on.

6 All Creatures of Our God and King

FRANCIS OF ASSISI
Translated by W. H. DRAPER

GEISTLICHE KIRCHENGESANG

Praise Him! Praise Him!

FANNY J. CROSBY

CHESTER G. ALLEN

1. Praise Him! praise Him! Je-sus, our bless-ed Re-deem-er! Sing, O Earth, His
2. Praise Him! praise Him! Je-sus, our bless-ed Re-deem-er! For our sins He
3. Praise Him! praise Him! Je-sus, our bless-ed Re-deem-er! Heavenly por-tals

won-der-ful love pro-claim! Hail Him! hail Him! highest archangels in glo-ry;
suffered, and bled, and died; He our Rock, our hope of e-ter-nal sal-va-tion,
loud with ho-san-nas ring! Je-sus, Sav-iour, reigneth for-ev-er and ev-er;

Strength and hon-or give to His ho-ly name! Like a shep-herd, Je-sus will
Hail Him! hail Him! Je-sus the Cru-ci-fied. Sound His prais-es! Je-sus who
Crown Him! crown Him! Prophet, and Priest, and King! Christ is com-ing! o-ver the

REFRAIN

guard His children, In His arms He carries them all day long:
bore our sor-rows, Love unbounded, wonderful, deep and strong: Praise Him! praise Him!
world vic-to-rious, Power and glo-ry un-to the Lord be-long:

tell of His ex-cel-lent greatness: Praise Him! praise Him! ev-er in joy-ful song!

Faith of Our Fathers

FREDERICK W. FABER

HENRY F. HEMY

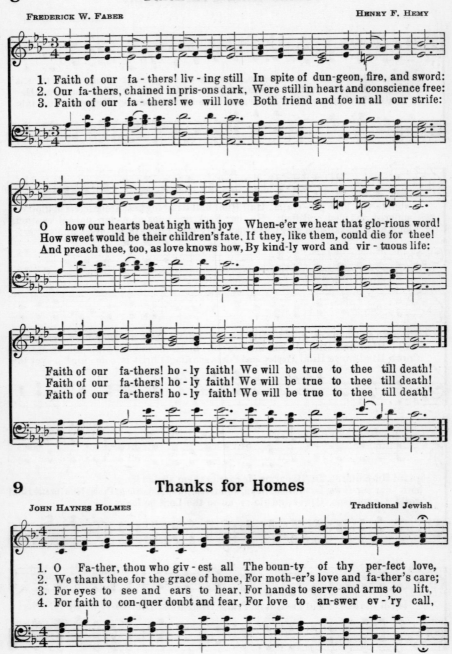

1. Faith of our fa-thers! liv-ing still In spite of dun-geon, fire, and sword:
2. Our fa-thers, chained in pris-ons dark, Were still in heart and conscience free:
3. Faith of our fa-thers! we will love Both friend and foe in all our strife:

O how our hearts beat high with joy When-e'er we hear that glo-rious word!
How sweet would be their children's fate, If they, like them, could die for thee!
And preach thee, too, as love knows how, By kind-ly word and vir-tuous life:

Faith of our fa-thers! ho-ly faith! We will be true to thee till death!
Faith of our fa-thers! ho-ly faith! We will be true to thee till death!
Faith of our fa-thers! ho-ly faith! We will be true to thee till death!

9

Thanks for Homes

JOHN HAYNES HOLMES

Traditional Jewish

1. O Fa-ther, thou who giv-est all The boun-ty of thy per-fect love,
2. We thank thee for the grace of home, For moth-er's love and fa-ther's care;
3. For eyes to see and ears to hear, For hands to serve and arms to lift,
4. For faith to con-quer doubt and fear, For love to an-swer ev-'ry call,

Thanks for Homes

We thank thee that up-on us fall Such ten-der bless-ings from a-bove.
For friends and teachers—all who come Our joys and hopes and fears to share.
For shoul-ders broad and strong to bear, For feet to run on er-rands swift.
For strength to do, and will to dare, We thank thee, O thou Lord of all.

My Faith Looks Up to Thee

10

RAY PALMER

LOWELL MASON

1. My faith looks up to Thee, Thou Lamb of Cal-va-ry,
2. May Thy rich grace im-part Strength to my faint-ing heart,
3. While life's dark maze I tread, And griefs a-round me spread,
4. When ends life's tran-sient dream, When death's cold, sul-len stream

Sav-iour di-vine! Now hear me while I pray, Take all my
My zeal in-spire; As Thou hast died for me, O may my
Be Thou my guide; Bid dark-ness turn to day, Wipe sor-row's
Shall o'er me roll; Blest Sav-iour, then, in love, Fear and dis-

guilt a-way, O let me from this day Be whol-ly Thine!
love to Thee Pure, warm and change-less be, A liv-ing fire!
tears a-way, Nor let me ev-er stray From Thee a-side.
trust re-move; O bear me safe a-bove, A ran-somed soul!

11 **All Hail the Power**

EDWARD PERRONET   OLIVER HOLDEN

1. All hail the power of Je - sus' name! Let an - gels pros - trate fall;
2. Ye cho - sen seed of Is - rael's race, Ye ran - somed from the fall,
3. Let ev - 'ry kin - dred, ev - 'ry tribe, On this ter - res - trial ball,
4. O that with yon - der sa - cred throng We at His feet may fall!

Bring forth the roy - al di - a - dem, And crown Him Lord of all;
Hail Him who saves you by His grace, And crown Him Lord of all;
To Him all maj - es - ty as - cribe, And crown Him Lord of all;
We'll join the ev - er - last - ing song, And crown Him Lord of all;

Bring forth the roy - al di - a - dem, And crown Him Lord of all!
Hail Him who saves you by His grace, And crown Him Lord of all!
To Him all maj - es - ty as - cribe, And crown Him Lord of all!
We'll join the ev - er - last - ing song, And crown Him Lord of all!

12 **How Lovely Is Thy Dwelling Place**

From PSALM 84   Adapted from J. MICHAEL HAYDN
Scottish Psalter

1. How love - ly is Thy dwell - ing - place, O Lord of hosts, to me!
2. My thirst - y soul longs ar - dent - ly, Yea, faints Thy courts to see:
3. Be - hold, the spar - row find - eth out An house where - in to rest;
4. Blest are they in Thy house that dwell, They ev - er give Thee praise.

How Lovely Is Thy Dwelling Place

The tab-er-nac-les of Thy grace, How pleas-ant, Lord, they be!
My ver-y heart and flesh cry out, O liv-ing God, for Thee.
The swal-low al-so for her-self Pro-vid-ed hath a nest;
Blest is the man whose strength Thou art, In whose heart are Thy ways.

Lead On, O King Eternal 13

ERNEST W. SHURTLEFF

HENRY SMART

1. Lead on, O King E-ter-nal, The day of march has come; Henceforth in fields of
2. Lead on, O King E-ter-nal, Till sin's fierce war shall cease, And ho-li-ness shall
3. Lead on, O King E-ter-nal, We fol-low, not with fears; For gladness breaks like

con-quest Thy tents shall be our home. Thro' days of prep-a-ra-tion Thy
whis-per The sweet A-men of peace; For not with swords loud clashing, Nor
morn-ing Where'er Thy face ap-pears; Thy cross is lift-ed o'er us; We

grace has made us strong, And now, O King E-ter-nal, We lift our bat-tle song.
roll of stirring drums; With deeds of love and mercy, The heavenly kingdom comes.
jour-ney in its light: The crown a waits the conquest; Lead on, O God of might.

14   O Worship the King

ROBERT GRANT

J. MICHAEL HAYDN

1. O wor-ship the King, all glo-rious 'a-bove, O grate-ful-ly
2. O tell of His might, O sing of His grace, Whose robe is the
3. Thy boun-ti-ful care, what tongue can re-cite? It breathes in the
4. Frail chil-dren of dust, and fee-ble as frail, In Thee do we

sing His pow-er and His love; Our Shield and De-fend-er, the
light, whose can-o-py space, His char-iots of wrath the deep
air; it shines in the light; It streams from the hills; it de-
trust, nor find Thee to fail; Thy mer-cies how ten-der! how

An-cient of Days, Pa-vil-ioned in splen-dor, and gird-ed with praise.
thun-der-clouds form, And dark is His path on the wings of the storm.
scends to the plain; And sweet-ly dis-tils in the dew and the rain.
firm to the end! Our Mak-er, De-fend-er, Re-deem-er and Friend!

15   All Things Praise Thee, Lord Most High

GEORGE W. COUDER

Unknown

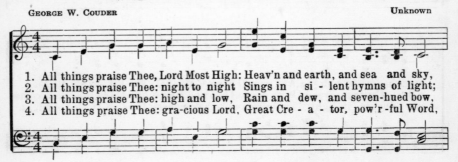

1. All things praise Thee, Lord Most High: Heav'n and earth, and sea and sky,
2. All things praise Thee: night to night Sings in si-lent hymns of light;
3. All things praise Thee: high and low, Rain and dew, and seven-hued bow,
4. All things praise Thee: gra-cious Lord, Great Cre-a-tor, pow'r-ful Word,

All Things Praise Thee, Lord Most High

All were for Thy glo - ry made, That Thy great-ness thus dis-played.
All things praise Thee: day to day Chants Thy pow'r in burn - ing ray;
Crim-son sun - set, flee - cy cloud, Rip - pling stream, and tem - pest loud,
Om - ni - pres - ent Spir - it, now At Thy feet we hum - bly bow;

Should all wor - ship bring to Thee; All things praise Thee: Lord, may we.
Time and space are prais-ing Thee; All things praise Thee: Lord, may we.
Sum - mer, win - ter, all to Thee; Glo - ry ren - der: Lord, may we.
Lift our hearts in praise to Thee; All things praise Thee: Lord, may we.

Praise Song 16

PSALM: 100

ANNIE RUTH RAUSCHENBERG

Make a joy - ful noise un - to the Lord, And come be-

fore His pres - ence with sing - ing; For He is good, His

mer - cy ev - er - last - ing; Praise the Lord and bless His name.

17 God of Our Fathers, Whose Almighty Hand

DANIEL C. ROBERTS

GEORGE W. WARREN

1. God of our fa-thers, whose al-might-y hand
2. Thy love di-vine hath led us in the past,
3. From war's a-larms, from dead-ly pes - ti - lence,
4. Re - fresh thy peo - ple on their toil-some way,

Leads forth in beau - ty all the star-ry band   Of shin-ing worlds in
In this free land by Thee our lot is cast;   Be Thou our rul - er,
Be Thy strong arm our ev - er sure de-fense;   Thy true re - lig - ion
Lead us from night to nev - er - end-ing day;   Fill all our lives with

splen-dor thro' the skies,   Our grate-ful songs be-fore Thy throne a - rise.
guardian, guide and stay,   Thy Word our law, Thy paths our cho-sen way.
in our hearts in-crease,   Thy bounteous goodness nour-ish us in peace.
love and grace di-vine,   And glo-ry, laud, and praise be ev - er Thine.

18 Doxology

THOMAS KEN

LOUIS BOURGEOIS

Praise God, from whom all blessings flow; Praise Him, all crea-tures here be - low;

Doxology

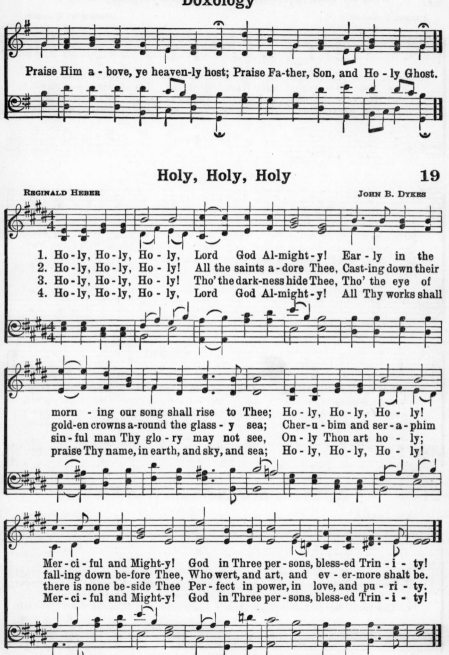

Praise Him a-bove, ye heaven-ly host; Praise Fa-ther, Son, and Ho-ly Ghost.

Holy, Holy, Holy

19

REGINALD HEBER

JOHN B. DYKES

1. Ho-ly, Ho-ly, Ho-ly, Lord God Al-might-y! Ear-ly in the
2. Ho-ly, Ho-ly, Ho-ly! All the saints a-dore Thee, Cast-ing down their
3. Ho-ly, Ho-ly, Ho-ly! Tho' the dark-ness hide Thee, Tho' the eye of
4. Ho-ly, Ho-ly, Ho-ly, Lord God Al-might-y! All Thy works shall

morn - ing our song shall rise to Thee; Ho-ly, Ho-ly, Ho - ly!
gold-en crowns a-round the glass - y sea; Cher-u-bim and ser-a-phim
sin-ful man Thy glo-ry may not see, On-ly Thou art ho - ly;
praise Thy name, in earth, and sky, and sea; Ho-ly, Ho-ly, Ho - ly!

Mer-ci-ful and Might-y! God in Three per-sons, bless-ed Trin-i-ty!
fall-ing down be-fore Thee, Who wert, and art, and ev-er-more shalt be.
there is none be-side Thee Per-fect in power, in love, and pu-ri-ty.
Mer-ci-ful and Might-y! God in Three per-sons, bless-ed Trin-i-ty!

20   Come, Thou Almighty King

Unknown   FELICE DE GIARDINI

1. Come, Thou Al - might - y King, Help us Thy name to sing,
2. Come, Thou In - car - nate Word, Gird on Thy might - y sword,
3. Come, Ho - ly Com - fort - er, Thy sa - cred wit - ness bear
4. To the great One in Three E - ter - nal prais - es be

Help us to praise: Fa - ther, all - glo - ri - ous, O'er all vic -
Our prayer at - tend: Come, and Thy peo - ple bless, And give Thy
In this glad hour: Thou who al - might - y art, Now rule in
Hence ev - er - more. His sov - reign maj - es - ty May we in

to - ri - ous, Come, and reign o - ver us, An - cient of Days.
Word suc-cess; Spir - it of ho - li - ness, On us de - scend.
ev - 'ry heart, And ne'er from us de - part, Spir - it of pow'r.
glo - ry see, And to e - ter - ni - ty Love and a - dore.

21   At Even, Ere the Sun Was Set

HENRY TWELLS   GEORG JOSEPHI

1. At e - ven, ere the sun was set, The sick, O Lord, a-round Thee lay;
2. Once more 'tis e-ven-tide and we, Oppressed with va-rious ills, draw near:
3. O Sav-iour Christ, our woes dis - pel; For some are sick and some are sad,
4. Thy touch has still its an-cient pow'r, No word from Thee can fruit-less fall;

At Even Ere the Sun Was Set

O in what di - vers pains they met! O with what joy they went a - way!
What if Thy form we can - not see? We know and feel that Thou art here.
And some have nev - er loved Thee well, And some have lost the love they had.
Hear, in this sol - emn eve - ning hour, And in Thy mer - cy heal us all.

Fairest Lord Jesus 22

Unknown   Arranged by R. S. WILLIS

1. Fair - est Lord Je - sus, Rul - er of all na - ture,
2. Fair are the mead - ows, Fair - er still the wood - lands,
3. Fair is the sun - shine, Fair - er still the moon - light,
4. Beau - ti - ful Sav - iour! Lord of all the na - tions!

O Thou of God and man the Son, Thee will I cher - ish,
Robed in the bloom - ing garb of spring; Je - sus is fair - er,
And all the twin - kling star - ry host; Je - sus shines bright-er,
Son of God and Son of man! Glo - ry and hon - or,

Thee will I hon - or, Thou my soul's glo - ry, joy, and crown.
Je - sus is pur - er, Who makes the woe - ful heart to sing.
Je - sus shines pur - er, Than all the an - gels heaven can boast.
Praise, a - do - ra - tion, Now and for - ev - er - more be Thine.

Joy to the World!

ISAAC WATTS

GEORGE F. HANDEL

1. Joy to the world! the Lord is come; Let earth re-
2. Joy to the earth! the Sav - iour reigns; Let men their
3. No more let sins and sor - rows grow, Nor thorns in-
4. He rules the world with truth and grace, And makes the

ceive her King; Let ev - er - y heart pre - pare Him room,
songs em - ploy; While fields and floods, rocks, hills and plains
fest the ground; He comes to make His bless - ings flow
na - tions prove The glo - ries of His right - eous - ness,

And heaven and na - ture sing, And heaven and na - ture
Re - peat the sound - ing joy, Re - peat the sound - ing
Far as the curse is found, Far as the curse is
And won - ders of His love, And won - ders of His

1. And heaven and na - ture sing,............ And

sing, And heaven, and heaven and na - ture sing.
joy, Re - peat, re - peat the sound - ing joy.
found, Far as, far as the curse is found.
love, And won - ders, and won - ders of His love.

heaven and na - ture sing,

It Came upon the Midnight Clear

EDMUND H. SEARS

RICHARD S. WILLIS

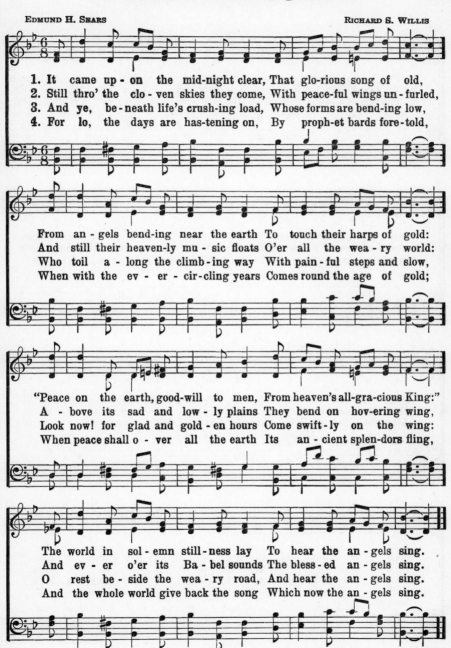

1. It came up-on the mid-night clear, That glo-rious song of old,
2. Still thro' the clo-ven skies they come, With peace-ful wings un-furled,
3. And ye, be-neath life's crush-ing load, Whose forms are bend-ing low,
4. For lo, the days are has-tening on, By proph-et bards fore-told,

From an-gels bend-ing near the earth To touch their harps of gold:
And still their heaven-ly mu-sic floats O'er all the wea-ry world:
Who toil a-long the climb-ing way With pain-ful steps and slow,
When with the ev-er-cir-cling years Comes round the age of gold;

"Peace on the earth, good-will to men, From heaven's all-gra-cious King:"
A-bove its sad and low-ly plains They bend on hov-ering wing,
Look now! for glad and gold-en hours Come swift-ly on the wing:
When peace shall o-ver all the earth Its an-cient splen-dors fling,

The world in sol-emn still-ness lay To hear the an-gels sing.
And ev-er o'er its Ba-bel sounds The bless-ed an-gels sing.
O rest be-side the wea-ry road, And hear the an-gels sing.
And the whole world give back the song Which now the an-gels sing.

25 Christ the Saviour Is Born

BLOSSOM BENNETT

FAITH CHAMBERS WILSON

1. The stars shin-ing down from the heav-ens were bright; Good shep-herds were
2. A dear Ba-by slept on the soft, fra-grant hay; And Ma-ry, His
3. The same stars are shin-ing on cit-y and plain; To-day we are

keep-ing their flocks thro' the night; When an-gels in glo-ry came
moth-er, kept watch where He lay; While an-gels were sing-ing, their
sing-ing the an-gels' re-frain; While each heart re-joic-es, we

sing-ing the sto-ry of "Joy to the world, Christ the Sav-iour is
glad mes-sage bringing, "All glo-ry to God—Christ the Sav-iour is
lift our glad voic-es, "All glo-ry to God—Christ the Sav-iour is

born"— Of "Joy to the world, Christ the Sav-iour is born."
born— All glo-ry to God, Christ the Sav-iour is born."
born— All glo-ry to God, Christ the Sav-iour is born."

Bethlehem Lullaby

P. W. BLACKMER

Arranged from BRAHMS

1. Long a - go, there was born In the cit - y of Da - vid,
2. Je - sus came as a Child From His Fa - ther in heav - en,

A sweet, ho - ly Babe, Who was Je - sus our King.
And has shown us the way To be lov - ing and kind,

An - gels sang at His birth, To all men, peace on earth,
While the stars sang a - bove, Lull - a - by, God is love,

An - gels sang at His birth, To all men, peace on earth.
While the stars sang a - bove, Lull - a - by, God is love.

Thou Didst Leave Thy Throne

EMILY E. S. ELLIOTT   TIMOTHY R. MATTHEWS

1. Thou didst leave Thy throne And Thy king - ly crown, When Thou cam - est to earth for me; But in Beth - le - hem's home Was there found no room For Thy ho - ly na - tiv - i - ty.
2. Heav-en's arch - es rang When the an - gels sang, Pro-claim - ing Thy roy - al de - gree; But of low - ly birth Didst Thou come to earth, And in great hu - mil - i - ty.
3. The fox - es found rest, And the birds their nest In the shade of the for - est tree; But Thy couch was the sod, O Thou Son of God, In the des - erts of Gal - i - lee.
4. Thou cam - est, O Lord, With the liv - ing word That should set Thy peo - ple free; But with mock - ing scorn, And with crown of thorn, They bore Thee to Cal - va - ry.
5. When the heav - ens shall ring, And the an - gels sing, At Thy com - ing to vic - to - ry, Let Thy voice call me home, Say - ing, "Yet there is room, There is room at My side for thee."

REFRAIN

1-4. O come to my heart, Lord Je - sus, There is room in my heart for Thee.
5. My heart shall rejoice, Lord Je - sus, When Thou comest and call-est for me.

We Three Kings of Orient Are

J. H. H.

JOHN H. HOPKINS

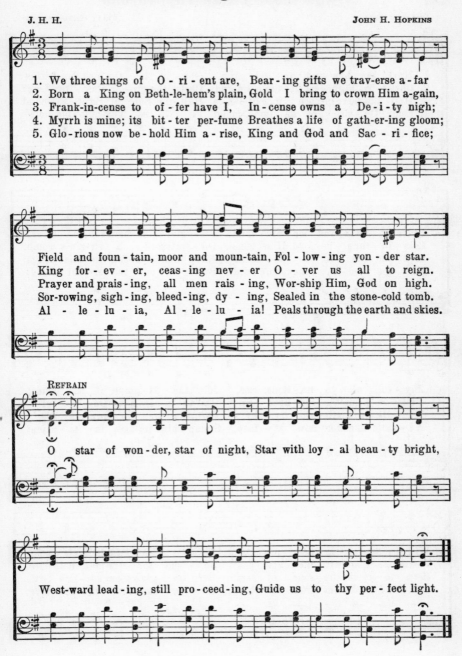

1. We three kings of O - ri - ent are, Bear - ing gifts we trav-erse a - far
2. Born a King on Beth-le-hem's plain, Gold I bring to crown Him a-gain,
3. Frank-in-cense to of - fer have I, In - cense owns a De - i - ty nigh;
4. Myrrh is mine; its bit - ter per-fume Breathes a life of gath-er-ing gloom;
5. Glo - rious now be - hold Him a - rise, King and God and Sac - ri - fice;

Field and foun - tain, moor and moun-tain, Fol - low - ing yon - der star.
King for - ev - er, ceas-ing nev - er O - ver us all to reign.
Prayer and prais - ing, all men rais - ing, Wor-ship Him, God on high.
Sor-rowing, sigh - ing, bleed-ing, dy - ing, Sealed in the stone-cold tomb.
Al - le - lu - ia, Al - le - lu - ia! Peals through the earth and skies.

REFRAIN

O star of won - der, star of night, Star with loy - al beau - ty bright,

West-ward lead - ing, still pro - ceed - ing, Guide us to thy per - fect light.

Hark! the Herald Angels Sing

CHARLES WESLEY

FELIX MENDELSSOHN

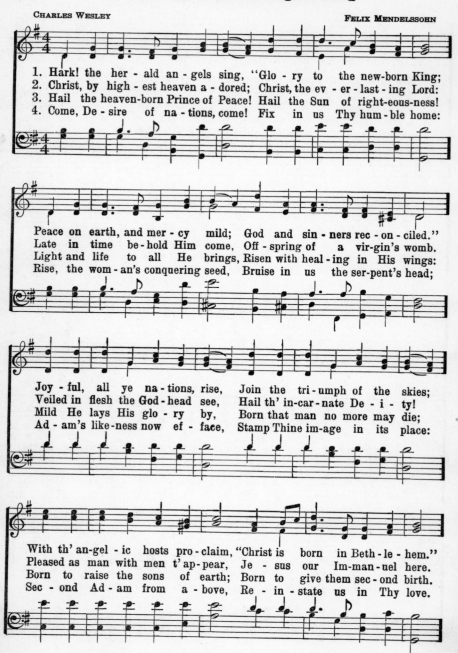

1. Hark! the her - ald an - gels sing, "Glo - ry to the new-born King;
2. Christ, by high - est heaven a - dored; Christ, the ev - er - last - ing Lord:
3. Hail the heaven-born Prince of Peace! Hail the Sun of right-eous-ness!
4. Come, De - sire of na - tions, come! Fix in us Thy hum - ble home:

Peace on earth, and mer - cy mild; God and sin - ners rec - on - ciled."
Late in time be - hold Him come, Off - spring of a vir-gin's womb.
Light and life to all He brings, Risen with heal - ing in His wings:
Rise, the wom - an's conquering seed, Bruise in us the ser-pent's head;

Joy - ful, all ye na - tions, rise, Join the tri - umph of the skies;
Veiled in flesh the God - head see, Hail th' in-car - nate De - i - ty!
Mild He lays His glo - ry by, Born that man no more may die;
Ad - am's like -ness now ef - face, Stamp Thine im-age in its place:

With th' an-gel - ic hosts pro - claim, "Christ is born in Beth - le - hem."
Pleased as man with men t' ap-pear, Je - sus our Im-man-uel here.
Born to raise the sons of earth; Born to give them sec - ond birth.
Sec - ond Ad - am from a - bove, Re - in - state us in Thy love.

Hark! the Herald Angels Sing

Hark! the her-ald an-gels sing, "Glo-ry to the new-born King."

O Come, All Ye Faithful

Translated by FREDERICK OAKELEY

WADE'S "Cantus Diversi"

1. O come, all ye faith-ful, joy-ful and tri-um-phant, O
2. Sing, choirs of an-gels, sing in ex-ul-ta-tion, O
3. Yea, Lord, we greet Thee, born this hap-py morn-ing,

come ye, O come ye to Beth-le-hem; Come and be-hold Him
sing, all ye bright hosts of heaven a-bove; Glo-ry to God, all
Je-sus, to Thee be all glo-ry given; Word of the Fa-ther,

REFRAIN

born the King of an-gels;
glo-ry in the high-est; O come, let us a-dore Him, O
now in flesh ap-pear-ing;

come, let us a-dore Him, O come, let us a-dore Him, Christ, the Lord.

The First Noel the Angel Did Say

Traditional   Traditional

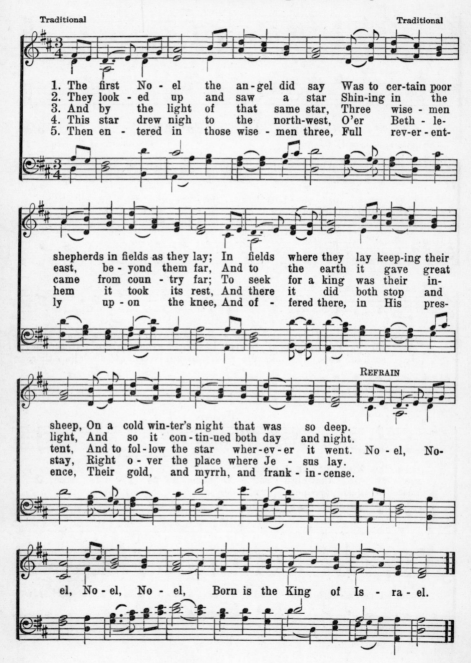

1. The first No - el the an-gel did say Was to cer-tain poor
2. They look - ed up and saw a star Shin-ing in the
3. And by the light of that same star, Three wise - men
4. This star drew nigh to the north-west, O'er Beth - le -
5. Then en - tered in those wise - men three, Full rev-er-ent-

shepherds in fields as they lay; In fields where they lay keep-ing their
east, be - yond them far, And to the earth it gave great
came from coun - try far; To seek for a king was their in -
hem it took its rest, And there it did both stop and
ly up - on the knee, And of - fered there, in His pres-

REFRAIN

sheep, On a cold win-ter's night that was so deep.
light, And so it con-tin-ued both day and night.
tent, And to fol-low the star wher-ev-er it went. No - el, No -
stay, Right o - ver the place where Je - sus lay.
ence, Their gold, and myrrh, and frank - in - cense.

el, No - el, No - el, Born is the King of Is - ra - el.

O Little Town of Bethlehem

PHILLIPS BROOKS

LEWIS H. REDNER

1. O lit-tle town of Bethlehem, How still we see thee lie! A-bove thy deep and
2. For Christ is born of Ma-ry; And gathered all a-bove, While mortals sleep, the
3. How si-lent-ly, How si-lent-ly The wondrous gift is given! So God im-parts to
4. O ho-ly Child of Bethlehem, De-scend to us, we pray; Cast out our sin and

dreamless sleep The si-lent stars go by; Yet in thy dark steets shin-eth The
an-gels keep Their watch of wond'ring love. O morning stars, to-geth-er Pro-
hu-man hearts The blessings of His heaven. No ear may hear His com-ing; But
en-ter in,—Be born in us to-day. We hear the Christmas an-gels The

ev-er-last-ing Light; The hopes and fears of all the years Are met in thee to-night.
claim the ho-ly birth, And praises sing to God the King, And peace to men on earth.
in this world of sin, Where meek souls will receive Him still, The dear Christ enters in.
great glad tidings tell, O come to us, a-bide with us, Our Lord Em-man-u-el.

What Can I Give

CHRISTINA G. ROSSETTI

Arranged from a Danish Folk-song

What can I give Him, Poor as I am? If I were a shep-herd, I would bring a lamb,

If I were a wise man I would do my part,— Yet what can I give Him, Give my heart.

34 Silent Night, Holy Night

JOSEPH MOHR

FRANZ GRÜBER

1. Si - lent night, ho - ly night, All is calm, all is bright
2. Si - lent night, ho - ly night, Dark-ness flies, all is light;
3. Si - lent night, ho - ly night, Guid - ing Star, lend thy light;
4. Si - lent night, ho - ly night, Won-drous Star, lend thy light;

Round yon Vir - gin Moth-er and Child, Ho - ly In-fant so ten-der and mild,
Shep -herds hear the an - gels sing, "Al - le - lu - ia! hail the King!
See the east-ern wise men bring Gifts and hom - age to our King!
With the an - gels let us sing Al - le - lu - ia to our King!

Sleep in heav - en - ly peace, Sleep in heav - en - ly peace.
Christ the Sav - iour is born, Christ the Sav - iour is born."
Christ the Sav - iour is born, Christ the Sav - iour is born.
Christ the Sav - iour is born, Christ the Sav - iour is born.

35 I Heard the Bells on Christmas Day

HENRY W. LONGFELLOW

J. BAPTISTE CALKIN

1. I heard the bells on Christ-mas day Their old fa - mil - iar car - ols play,
2. I thought how, as the day had come, The bel-fries of all Chris-ten-dom
3. And in de-spair I bowed my head: "There is no peace on earth," I said;
4. Then pealed the bells more loud and deep: "God is not dead, nor doth He sleep;
5. Till, ring-ing, sing-ing on its way, The world re-volved from night to day,

I Heard the Bells on Christmas Day

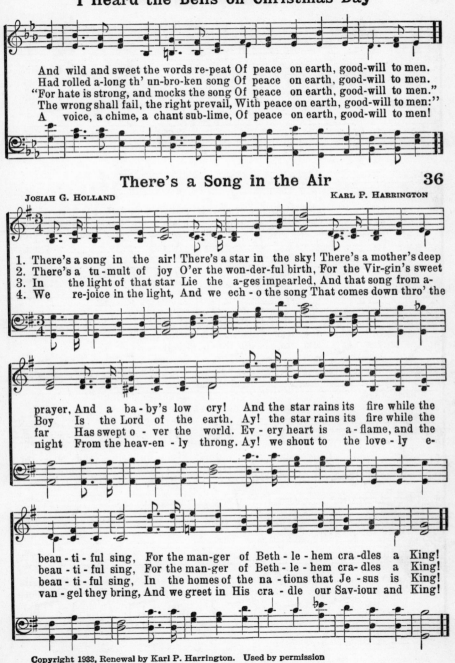

And wild and sweet the words re-peat Of peace on earth, good-will to men.
Had rolled a-long th' un-bro-ken song Of peace on earth, good-will to men.
"For hate is strong, and mocks the song Of peace on earth, good-will to men."
The wrong shall fail, the right prevail, With peace on earth, good-will to men:"
A voice, a chime, a chant sub-lime, Of peace on earth, good-will to men!

There's a Song in the Air 36

JOSIAH G. HOLLAND

KARL P. HARRINGTON

1. There's a song in the air! There's a star in the sky! There's a mother's deep
2. There's a tu-mult of joy O'er the won-der-ful birth, For the Vir-gin's sweet
3. In the light of that star Lie the a-ges impearled, And that song from a-
4. We re-joice in the light, And we ech-o the song That comes down thro' the

prayer, And a ba-by's low cry! And the star rains its fire while the
Boy Is the Lord of the earth. Ay! the star rains its fire while the
far Has swept o-ver the world. Ev-ery heart is a-flame, and the
night From the heav-en-ly throng. Ay! we shout to the love-ly e-

beau-ti-ful sing, For the man-ger of Beth-le-hem cra-dles a King!
beau-ti-ful sing, For the man-ger of Beth-le-hem cra-dles a King!
beau-ti-ful sing, In the homes of the na-tions that Je-sus is King!
van-gel they bring, And we greet in His cra-dle our Sav-iour and King!

O Holy Night

ADOLF ADAM
Arranged by B. B. McKINNEY

1. O ho - ly night; The stars are bright-ly shin - ing; It is the night of the dear Sav - iour's birth; Long lay the world in sin and er - ror pin - - ing, Till He ap-peared, and the soul felt His
2. Led by .... the light Of faith se-rene-ly beam - ing, With glow-ing hearts by His cra - dle to stand; Led by the light of the star so bright-ly gleam - ing, Here came the wise men from O - ri - ent

O Holy Night

worth; . . . . .
land; . . . . . A thrill of hope, the wea - ry world re-

joic - es, For yon - der breaks a new and cloud-less morn!

Fall on your knees, O hear the an - gel voic - es, O

night di - vine! . . . . O night . . . when Christ was born! O
O night di-vine! O night was born!

night . . . di - vine! . . . . O night, O night di - vine!
O night

38 While Shepherds Watched Their Flocks

NAHUM TATE   GEORGE F. HANDEL

1. While shep-herds watched their flocks by night, All seat-ed
2. "Fear not!" said he; for might-y dread Had seized their
3. "To you, in Da-vid's town, this day Is born, of
4. "All glo-ry be to God on high, And to the

on the ground, The an-gel of the Lord came down,
trou-bled mind, "Glad ti-dings of great joy I bring,
Da-vid's line, The Sav-iour, who is Christ the Lord;
earth be peace: Good-will hence-forth from heav'n to men,

And glo-ry shone a-round, And glo-ry shone a-round.
To you and all man-kind, To you and all man-kind.
And this shall be the sign: And this shall be the sign:
Be-gin and nev-er cease, Be-gin and nev-er cease!"

39 Angels, from the Realms of Glory

JAMES MONTGOMERY   HENRY SMART

1. An-gels, from the realms of glo-ry, Wing your flight o'er all the earth,
2. Shep-herds, in the field a-bid-ing, Watch-ing o'er your flocks by night,
3. Sag-es, leave your con-tem-pla-tions, Bright-er vi-sions beam a-far;
4. Saints be-fore the al-tar bend-ing, Watch-ing long in hope and fear;

Angels, from the Realms of Glory

Ye, who sang cre - a - tion's sto - ry, Now pro-claim Mes - si - ah's birth:
God with man is now re - sid - ing, Yon-der shines the In - fant-Light;
Seek the great De - sire of na - tions, Ye have seen His na - tal star;
Sud - den - ly the Lord, de - scend-ing, In His tem - ple shall ap - pear;

Come and wor-ship, come and wor-ship, Wor - ship Christ, the new-born King.

Away in a Manger

40

M. L.

MARTIN LUTHER

1. A - way in a man - ger, No crib for a bed, The lit - tle Lord
2. The cat - tle are low - ing, The Ba - by a - wakes, But lit - tle Lord
3. Be near me, Lord Je - sus, I ask Thee to stay Close by me for -

Je - sus Laid down His sweet head; The stars in the sky Looked
Je - sus, No cry - ing He makes; I love Thee, Lord Je - sus! Look
ev - er, And love me, I pray; Bless all the dear chil-dren In

down where He lay,—The lit - tle Lord Je - sus, A - sleep on the hay.
down from the sky, And stay by my cra - dle, Till morn-ing is nigh.
Thy ten - der care, And take us to heav - en, To live with Thee there.

O Jesus, Once a Nazareth Boy

Unknown

HENRY S. CUTLER

1. O Je-sus, once a Naz-areth boy, And tempt-ed like as we,
2. O Je-sus, Prince of life and truth, Be-neath thy ban-ner bright,

All in-ward foes help us de-stroy And spot-less all to be.
We ded-i-cate our strength and youth To bat-tle for the right;

We trust thee for the grace to win The high vic-to-rious goal,
We give our lives with glad in-tent To serve the world and Thee,

Where pu-ri-ty shall con-quer sin In Christ-like self-con-trol.
To die, to suf-fer, or be spent To set our broth-ers free.

In the Temple

42

FLORA KIRKLAND

HOWARD E. SMITH

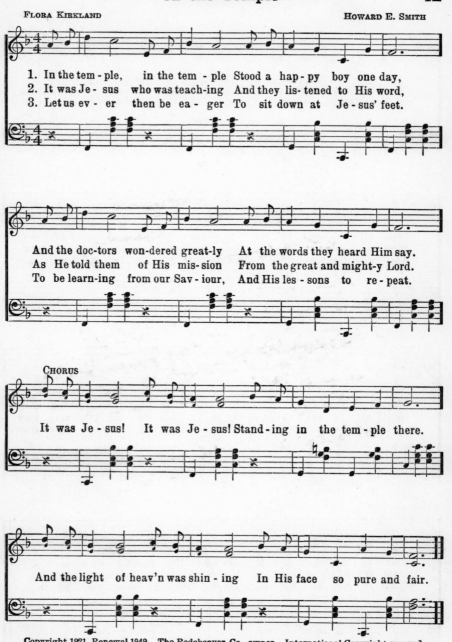

1. In the tem - ple, in the tem - ple Stood a hap - py boy one day,
2. It was Je - sus who was teach-ing And they lis- tened to His word,
3. Let us ev - er then be ea - ger To sit down at Je - sus' feet.

And the doc-tors won-dered great-ly At the words they heard Him say.
As He told them of His mis- sion From the great and might-y Lord.
To be learn-ing from our Sav - iour, And His les - sons to re - peat.

CHORUS

It was Je - sus! It was Je - sus! Stand-ing in the tem - ple there.

And the light of heav'n was shin - ing In His face so pure and fair.

43　O Master Workman of the Race

JAY T. STOCKING

Henry S. CUTLER

1. O Mas - ter work-man of the race, Thou Man of Gal - i - lee,
2. O Car - pen - ter of Naz - a - reth, Build - er of life di - vine,
3. O Thou who didst the vis - ion send, And gives to each his task,

Who with the eyes of ear - ly youth E - ter - nal things did see,
Who shap - est man to God's own law, Thy-self the fair de - sign,
And with the task suf - fi - cient strength, Show us Thy will, we ask;

We thank Thee for Thy boy-hood faith That shone Thy whole life thro';
Build us a tow'r of Christ-like height, That we the land may view,
Give us a con-science bold and good, Give us a pur - pose true,

"Did ye not know it is My work My Fa-ther's work to do?"
And see like Thee our no - blest work Our Fa-ther's work to do.
That it may be our high-est joy Our Fa-ther's work to do.

There Is a Green Hill Far Away

44

CECIL F. ALEXANDER

GEORGE C. STEBBINS

1. There is a green hill far a-way, With-out a cit-y wall,
2. We may not know, we can-not tell, What pains He had to bear;
3. He died that we might be for-given, He died to make us good,
4. There was no oth-er good e-nough To pay the price of sin,

Where the dear Lord was cru-ci-fied, Who died to save us all.
But we be-lieve it was for us He hung and suf-fered there.
That we might go at last to heaven, Saved by His pre-cious blood.
He on-ly could un-lock the gate Of heaven and let us in.

CHORUS

Oh, dear-ly, dear-ly has He loved, And we must love Him, too,

And trust in His re-deem-ing blood, And try His works to do.

The Old Rugged Cross

G. B.

GEORGE BENNARD

1. On a hill far a-way stood an old rug-ged cross, The em-blem of
2. Oh, that old rug-ged cross so de-spised by the world, Has a won-drous at-
3. In the old rug-ged cross, stained with blood so di-vine, A won-drous
4. To the old rug-ged cross I will ev-er be true, Its shame and re-

suf-fering and shame; And I love that old cross where the dear-est and best
trac-tion for me; For the dear Lamb of God left His glo-ry a-bove,
beau-ty I see; For 'twas on that old cross Je-sus suf-fered and died,
proach glad-ly bear; Then He'll call me some day to my home far a-way,

CHORUS

For a world of lost sin-ners was slain.
To bear it to dark Cal-va-ry. So I'll cher-ish the old rug-ged
To par-don and sanc-ti-fy me.
Where His glo-ry for-ev-er I'll share. cross, the

cross, . . . Till my tro-phies at last I lay down; I will cling to the
old rug-ged cross,

old rug-ged cross, . . . And ex-change it some day for a crown.
cross, the old rug-ged cross,

The Banner of the Cross

Daniel W. Whittle

James McGranahan

1. There's a roy - al ban - ner giv - en for dis-play To the sol - diers
2. Though the foe may rage and gath - er as the flood, Let the stand-ard
3. O - ver land and sea, wher-ev - er man may dwell, Make the glo - rious
4. When the glo - ry dawns—'tis draw-ing ver - y near—It is has-tening

of the King; As an en - sign fair we lift it up to-day,
be dis - played; And be-neath its folds, as sol-diers of the Lord,
ti - dings known; Of the crim - son ban - ner now the sto - ry tell,
day by day— Then be-fore our King the foe shall dis - ap-pear,

Chorus

While as ran-somed ones we sing.
For the truth be not dis - mayed! March-ing on, . . . march-ing
While the Lord shall claim His own!
And the cross the world shall sway!

on, on,

on, . . . For Christ count ev - ery-thing but loss! . . . . . And to
on, on, ev - ery-thing, ev - ery-thing but loss!

crown Him King, toil and sing 'Neath the ban - ner of the cross!
we'll Be - neath

I Gave My Life for Thee

FRANCES R. HAVERGAL

PHILIP P. BLISS

1. I gave My life for thee, My pre-cious blood I shed,
2. My Fa-ther's house of light,— My glo-ry-cir-cled throne,—
3. I suf-fered much for thee, More than thy tongue can tell,
4. And I have brought to thee, Down from My home a-bove,

That thou might'st ran-somed be, And quick-ened from the dead;
I left for earth-ly night, For wan-derings sad and lone;
Of bit-terest ag-o-ny, To res-cue thee from hell;
Sal-va-tion full and free, My par-don and My love;

I gave, I gave My life for thee, What hast thou given for Me?
I left, I left it all for thee, Hast thou left aught for Me?
I've borne, I've borne it all for thee, What hast thou borne for Me?
I bring, I bring rich gifts to thee, What hast thou brought to Me?

48   When I Survey the Wondrous Cross

ISAAC WATTS

Arranged by LOWELL MASON

1. When I sur-vey the won-drous cross, On which the Prince of glo-ry died,
2. For-bid it, Lord! that I should boast, Save in the death of Christ my God:
3. See, from His head, His hands, His feet, Sor-row and love flow min-gled down:
4. Were the whole realm of na-ture mine, That were a pres-ent far too small;

When I Survey the Wondrous Cross

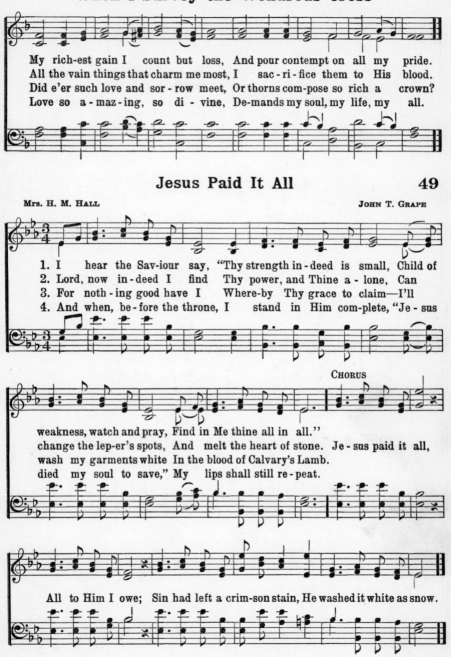

My rich-est gain I count but loss, And pour contempt on all my pride.
All the vain things that charm me most, I sac-ri-fice them to His blood.
Did e'er such love and sor-row meet, Or thorns com-pose so rich a crown?
Love so a-maz-ing, so di-vine, De-mands my soul, my life, my all.

Jesus Paid It All
49

Mrs. H. M. Hall

John T. Grape

1. I hear the Sav-iour say, "Thy strength in-deed is small, Child of
2. Lord, now in-deed I find Thy power, and Thine a-lone, Can
3. For noth-ing good have I Where-by Thy grace to claim—I'll
4. And when, be-fore the throne, I stand in Him com-plete, "Je-sus

Chorus

weakness, watch and pray, Find in Me thine all in all."
change the lep-er's spots, And melt the heart of stone. Je-sus paid it all,
wash my garments white In the blood of Calvary's Lamb.
died my soul to save," My lips shall still re-peat.

All to Him I owe; Sin had left a crim-son stain, He washed it white as snow.

Christ Arose

R. L.

ROBERT LOWRY

1. Low in the grave He lay— Je-sus my Sav-iour! Wait-ing the com-ing day—
2. Vain-ly they watch His bed— Je-sus my Sav-iour! Vain-ly they seal the dead—
3. Death cannot keep his prey— Je-sus my Sav-iour! He tore the bars a-way—

REFRAIN

Je-sus my Lord! Up from the grave He a-rose (He a-rose), With a

might-y tri-umph o'er His foes; (He a-rose!) He a-rose a Vic-tor from the

dark do-main, And He lives for-ev-er with His saints to reign. He a-

rose!   He a-rose!   Hal-le-lu-jah! Christ a-rose!

He a-rose!   He a-rose!

He Lives On High 51

B. B. McK.

Arranged by B. B. McKinney
From Hawaiian Folk Song

1. Christ the Sav - iour came from heaven's glo - ry, To re - deem the
2. He a - rose from death and all its sor - row, To dwell in that
3. Wea - ry soul, to Je - sus come con - fess - ing, Re - demp - tion from

lost from sin and shame; On His brow He wore the thorn-crown
land of joy and love; He is com - ing back some glad to-
sin He of - fers thee; Look to Je - sus and re - ceive a

go - ry, And up - on Cal - va - ry He took my blame.
mor - row, And He'll take all His chil-dren home a - bove.
bless - ing, There is life, there is joy and vic - to - ry.

CHORUS

He lives on high, He lives on high, Tri-um-phant o - ver sin and all its

stain; He lives on high, He lives on high, Some day He's com-ing a - gain.

52

He Lives

A. H. A.

A. H. ACKLEY

1. I serve a ris-en Sav-iour, He's in the world to-day; I know that He is
2. In all the world a-round me I see His lov-ing care, And tho' my heart grows
3. Rejoice, rejoice, O Christian, lift up your voice and sing E - ter - nal hal - le-

liv - ing, what-ev - er men may say; I see His hand of mer - cy, I
wea-ry I nev - er will de - spair; I know that He is lead-ing, thro'
lu - jahs to Je - sus Christ the King! The Hope of all who seek Him, the

hear His voice of cheer, And just the time I need Him He's al-ways near.
all the storm-y blast, The day of His ap-pear-ing will come at last.
Help of all who find, None oth-er is so lov-ing, so good and kind.

REFRAIN

He lives, He lives, Christ Je - sus lives to - day! He walks with me and
He lives, He lives,

talks with me a-long life's nar-row way. He lives, He lives, sal-
He lives, He lives,

He Lives

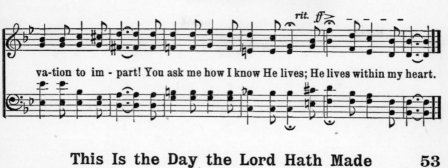

va-tion to im - part! You ask me how I know He lives; He lives within my heart.

This Is the Day the Lord Hath Made 53

ISAAC WATTS

LOWELL MASON

1. This is the day the Lord hath made, He calls the hours His own;
2. To - day He rose and left the dead, And Sa - tan's em - pire fell;
3. Ho - san - na, to th'a - noint - ed King, To Da - vid's ho - ly Son!
4. Blest be the Lord, who comes to men, With mes - sag - es of grace;

Let heav'n re - joice, let earth be glad, And praise sur-round the throne,
To - day the saints His tri-umphs spread, And all His won-ders tell,
Help us, O Lord; de - scend and bring Sal - va - tion from the throne,
Who comes in God His Fa-ther's name, To save our sin - ful race,

Let heav'n re - joice, let earth be glad, And praise sur-round the throne.
To - day the saints His triumph spread And all His won - ders tell.
Help us, O Lord; de-scend and bring Sal - va - tion from the throne.
Who comes in God His Fa-ther's name, To save our sin - ful race.

54 Christ the Lord Is Risen Today

CHARLES WESLEY

From "Lyra Davidica"

1. Christ the Lord is risen to - day, Al - - - le - lu - ia!
2. Lives a - gain our glo - rious King: Al - - - le - lu - ia!
3. Love's re - deem-ing work is done, Al - - - le - lu - ia!
4. Soar we now, where Christ has led, Al - - - le - lu - ia!

Sons of men and an - gels say: Al - - - le - lu - ia!
Where, O death, is now thy sting? Al - - - le - lu - ia!
Fought the fight, the bat - tle won; Al - - - le - lu - ia!
Fol - lowing our ex - alt - ed Head; Al - - - le - lu - ia!

Raise your joys and tri - umphs high, Al - - - le - lu - ia!
Dy - ing once, He all doth save: Al - - - le - lu - ia!
Death in vain for - bids Him rise; Al - - - le - lu - ia!
Made like Him, like Him we rise; Al - - - le - lu - ia!

Sing, ye heavens, and earth, re - ply, Al - - - le - lu - ia!
Where thy vic - to - ry, O grave? Al - - - le - lu - ia!
Christ has o - pened Par - a - dise. Al - - - le - lu - ia!
Ours the cross, the grave, the skies. Al - - - le - lu - ia!

The Son of God Goes Forth to War

REGINALD HEBER

HENRY S. CUTLER

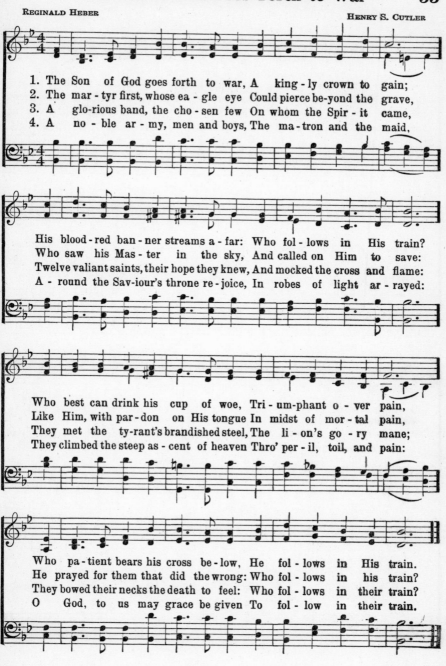

1. The Son of God goes forth to war, A king-ly crown to gain;
2. The mar-tyr first, whose ea-gle eye Could pierce be-yond the grave,
3. A glo-rious band, the cho-sen few On whom the Spir-it came,
4. A no-ble ar-my, men and boys, The ma-tron and the maid,

His blood-red ban-ner streams a-far: Who fol-lows in His train?
Who saw his Mas-ter in the sky, And called on Him to save:
Twelve valiant saints, their hope they knew, And mocked the cross and flame:
A-round the Sav-iour's throne re-joice, In robes of light ar-rayed:

Who best can drink his cup of woe, Tri-um-phant o-ver pain,
Like Him, with par-don on His tongue In midst of mor-tal pain,
They met the ty-rant's brandished steel, The li-on's go-ry mane;
They climbed the steep as-cent of heaven Thro' per-il, toil, and pain:

Who pa-tient bears his cross be-low, He fol-lows in His train.
He prayed for them that did the wrong: Who fol-lows in his train?
They bowed their necks the death to feel: Who fol-lows in their train?
O God, to us may grace be given To fol-low in their train.

56 Onward, Christian Soldiers

SABINE BARING-GOULD

ARTHUR SULLIVAN

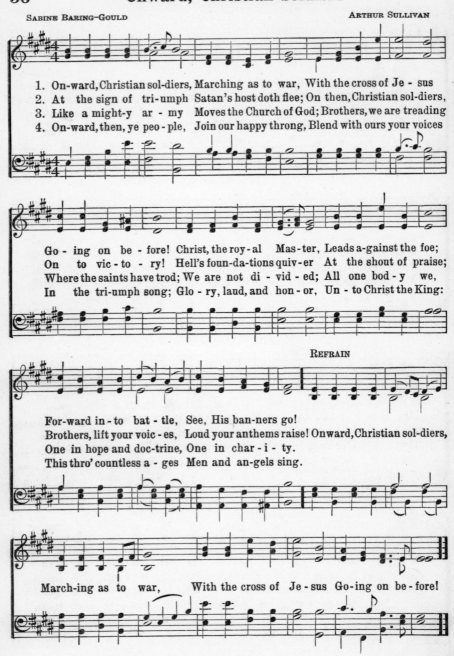

1. On-ward, Christian sol-diers, Marching as to war, With the cross of Je - sus
2. At the sign of tri-umph Satan's host doth flee; On then, Christian sol-diers,
3. Like a might-y ar - my Moves the Church of God; Brothers, we are treading
4. On-ward, then, ye peo - ple, Join our happy throng, Blend with ours your voices

Go - ing on be - fore! Christ, the roy-al Mas-ter, Leads a-gainst the foe;
On to vic - to - ry! Hell's foun-da-tions quiv-er At the shout of praise;
Where the saints have trod; We are not di - vid - ed; All one bod - y we,
In the tri-umph song; Glo - ry, laud, and hon - or, Un - to Christ the King:

REFRAIN

For-ward in - to bat - tle, See, His ban-ners go!
Brothers, lift your voic - es, Loud your anthems raise! Onward, Christian sol-diers,
One in hope and doc-trine, One in char - i - ty.
This thro' countless a - ges Men and an-gels sing.

March-ing as to war, With the cross of Je - sus Go-ing on be - fore!

Who Is on the Lord's Side?

FRANCES R. HAVERGAL

JOHN GOSS

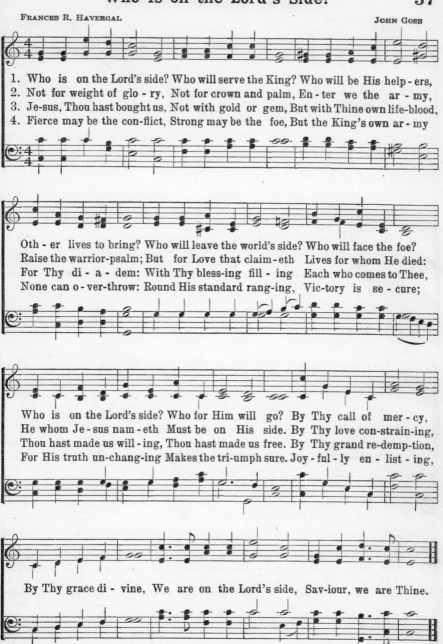

1. Who is on the Lord's side? Who will serve the King? Who will be His help-ers,
2. Not for weight of glo - ry, Not for crown and palm, En - ter we the ar - my,
3. Je-sus, Thou hast bought us, Not with gold or gem, But with Thine own life-blood,
4. Fierce may be the con-flict, Strong may be the foe, But the King's own ar - my

Oth - er lives to bring? Who will leave the world's side? Who will face the foe?
Raise the warrior-psalm; But for Love that claim-eth Lives for whom He died:
For Thy di - a - dem: With Thy bless-ing fill - ing Each who comes to Thee,
None can o - ver-throw: Round His standard rang-ing, Vic-tory is se - cure;

Who is on the Lord's side? Who for Him will go? By Thy call of mer - cy,
He whom Je - sus nam - eth Must be on His side. By Thy love con-strain-ing,
Thou hast made us will - ing, Thou hast made us free. By Thy grand re-demp-tion,
For His truth un-chang-ing Makes the tri-umph sure. Joy - ful - ly en - list - ing,

By Thy grace di - vine, We are on the Lord's side, Sav-iour, we are Thine.

58 Now in the Days of Youth

WALTER J. MATHAMS

GEORGE J. ELVEY

1. Now in the days of youth, When life flows fresh and free,
2. Teach us wher-e'er we live, To act as in Thy sight,
3. Teach us to love the true, The beau-ti-ful and pure,
4. Spir-it of Christ, do Thou Our first bright days in-spire,

Thou Lord of all our hearts and lives, We give our-selves to Thee;
And do what Thou wouldst have us do With ra-di-ant de-light;
And let us not for one short hour An e-vil thought en-dure;
That we may live the life of love And loft-i-est de-sire;

Our fer-vent gift re-ceive, And fit us to ful-fill.
Not choos-ing what is great, Nor spurn-ing what is small,
But give us grace to stand De-cid-ed, brave and strong,
And be by Thee pre-pared For larg-er years to come;

Thro' all our days, in all our ways, Our heav'n-ly Fa-ther's will.
But take as from Thy hands our tasks And glo-ri-fy them all.
The lov-ers of all ho-ly things, The foes of all things wrong.
And for the life in-ef-fa-ble With-in the Fa-ther's home.

Words from "The Pilgrim Hymnal." Copyright, The Pilgrim Press. Used by permission

Saviour, Like a Shepherd Lead Us

DOROTHY A. THRUPP

WILLIAM B. BRADBURY

1. Sav - iour, like a shep-herd lead us, Much we need Thy ten-der care;
2. We are Thine; do Thou be - friend us, Be the Guard-ian of our way;
3. Thou hast prom-ised to re - ceive us, Poor and sin - ful though we be;
4. Ear - ly let us seek Thy fa - vor; Ear - ly let us do Thy will;

In Thy pleas-ant pas-tures feed us, For our use Thy folds pre-pare:
Keep Thy flock, from sin de - fend us, Seek us when we go a - stray:
Thou hast mer-cy to re - lieve us, Grace to cleanse, and power to free:
Bless-ed Lord and on - ly Sav - iour, With Thy love our bos-oms fill:

Bless-ed Je - sus, Bless-ed Je - sus, Thou hast bought us, Thine we are;
Bless-ed Je - sus, Bless-ed Je - sus, Hear, O hear us when we pray;
Bless-ed Je - sus, Bless-ed Je - sus, Ear - ly let us turn to Thee;
Bless-ed Je - sus, Bless-ed Je - sus, Thou hast loved us, love us still;

Bless-ed Je - sus, Bless-ed Je - sus, Thou hast bought us, Thine we are.
Bless-ed Je - sus, Bless-ed Je - sus, Hear, O hear us when we pray.
Bless-ed Je - sus, Bless-ed Je - sus, Ear - ly let us turn to Thee.
Bless-ed Je - sus, Bless-ed Je - sus, Thou hast loved us, love us still.

60 Let Others See Jesus in You

B. B. McK.

B. B. McKinney

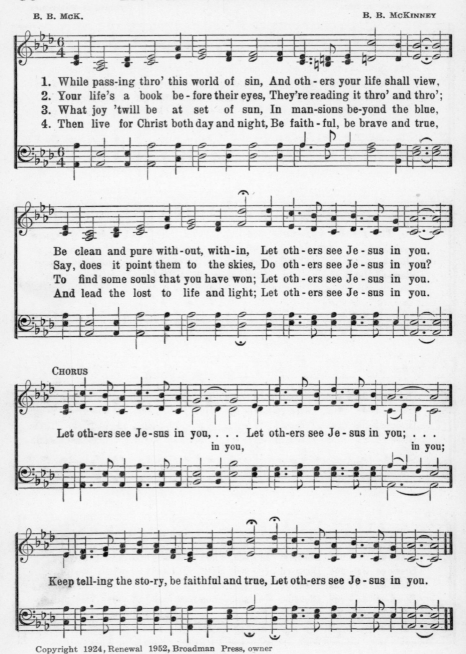

1. While pass-ing thro' this world of sin, And oth - ers your life shall view,
2. Your life's a book be - fore their eyes, They're reading it thro' and thro';
3. What joy 'twill be at set of sun, In man-sions be-yond the blue,
4. Then live for Christ both day and night, Be faith - ful, be brave and true,

Be clean and pure with-out, with-in, Let oth-ers see Je - sus in you.
Say, does it point them to the skies, Do oth-ers see Je - sus in you?
To find some souls that you have won; Let oth-ers see Je - sus in you.
And lead the lost to life and light; Let oth-ers see Je - sus in you.

CHORUS

Let oth-ers see Je-sus in you, . . . Let oth-ers see Je-sus in you; . . .
in you,   in you;

Keep tell-ing the sto-ry, be faithful and true, Let oth-ers see Je - sus in you.

Help Somebody Today

Mrs. Frank A. Breck   Charles H. Gabriel

1. Look all a-round you, find someone in need, Help some-bod-y to-day!
2. Man-y are wait-ing a kind, lov-ing word, Help some-bod-y to-day!
3. Man-y have bur-dens too heav-y to bear, Help some-bod-y to-day!
4. Some are dis-cour-aged and wear-y in heart, Help some-bod-y to-day!

Tho' it be lit-tle—a neigh-bor-ly deed—Help some-bod-y to-day!
Thou hast a mes-sage, O let it be heard, Help some-bod-y to-day!
Grief is the por-tion of some ev-'ry-where, Help some-bod-y to-day!
Some one the jour-ney to Heaven should start, Help some-bod-y to-day!

Chorus.

Help some-bod-y to-day, ... Some-bod-y a-long life's way; .... Let
to-day,   home-ward way;

sor-row be en-ded, The friendless be-friended, Oh, help somebody to-day!

I Would Be True

HOWARD ARNOLD WALTER

JOSEPH YATES PEEK

1. I would be true, for there are those that trust me; I would be
2. I would be friend of all—the foe, the friend-less; I would be
3. I would be prayer-ful thro' each bus-y mo-ment; I would be

pure, for there are those who care; I would be strong, for
giv - ing, and for - get the gift; I would be hum - ble,
con - stant - ly in touch with God; I would be tuned to

there is much to suf - fer; I would be brave, for there is
for I know my weak - ness; I would look up, and laugh, and
hear the slight - est whis - per; I would have faith to keep the

much to dare, I would be brave, for there is much to dare.
love, and lift, I would look up, and laugh, and love, and lift.
path Christ trod, I would have faith to keep the path Christ trod.

Soldiers of Christ, Arise

Charles Wesley

George J. Elvey

1. Sol - diers of Christ, a - rise, And put your arm - or on;
2. Stand, then, in His great might, With all His strength en - dued;
3. Leave no un-guard - ed place, No weak - ness of the soul,

Strong in the strength which God sup-plies Thro' his e - ter - nal Son;
And take, to arm you for the fight, The pan - o - ply of God;
Take ev - 'ry vir - tue, ev - 'ry grace, And for - ti - fy the whole.

Strong in the Lord of Hosts, And in his might - y power,
That, hav - ing all things done, And all your con - flicts past,
From strength to strength go on, Wres - tle and fight and pray;

Who in the strength of Je - sus trusts Is more than con-quer - or.
Ye may o'er-come, thro' Christ a - lone, And stand en - tire at last.
Tread all the pow'rs of dark - ness down And win the well-fought day.

64 Tell Me the Story of Jesus

FANNY J. CROSBY

JOHN R. SWENEY

1. Tell me the sto - ry of Je - sus, Write on my heart ev - ery word;
2. Fast-ing a - lone in the des - ert, Tell of the days that are past,
3. Tell of the cross where they nailed Him, Writh-ing in an-guish and pain;

CHO.—*Tell me the sto - ry of Je - sus, Write on my heart ev - ery word;*

FINE

Tell me the sto - ry most pre - cious, Sweet-est that ev - er was heard.
How for our sins He was tempt - ed, Yet was tri - um-phant at last.
Tell of the grave where they laid Him, Tell how He liv - eth a - gain.

Tell me the sto - ry most pre - cious, Sweet - est that ev - er was heard.

Tell how the an - gels, in cho - rus, Sang as they wel-comed His birth,
Tell of the years of His la - bor, Tell of the sor - row He bore;
Love in that sto - ry so ten - der, Clear - er than ev - er I see:

D. C. for Chorus

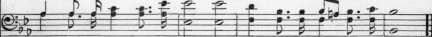

"Glo - ry to God in the high - est! Peace and good ti - dings to earth."
He was de-spised and af - flict - ed, Home-less, re - ject - ed and poor.
Stay, let me weep while you whis - per, Love paid the ran-som for me.

Give of Your Best to the Master

H. B. G.

Mrs. Charles Barnard

1. Give of your best to the Mas - ter; Give of the strength of your youth;
2. Give of your best to the Mas - ter; Give Him first place in your heart;
3. Give of your best to the Mas - ter; Naught else is wor - thy His love;

REF.—*Give of your best to the Mas - ter; Give of the strength of your youth:*

FINE

Throw your soul's fresh, glowing ar - dor In - to the bat - tle for truth.
Give Him first place in your serv - ice, Con - se - crate ev - 'ry part.
He gave Him - self for your ran - som, Gave up His glo - ry a - bove:

Clad in sal - va-tion's full ar - mor, Join in the bat - tle for truth.

Je - sus has set the ex - am - ple; Dauntless was He, young and brave;
Give, and to you shall be giv - en; God His be - lov - ed Son gave;
Laid down His life with-out mur - mur, You from sin's ru - in to save;

D.C. Ref.

Give Him your loy - al de - vo - tion, Give Him the best that you have. . .
Grate-ful - ly seek-ing to serve Him, Give Him the best that you have. . .
Give Him your heart's ad-o - ra - tion, Give Him the best that you have. . .

A Friend of Jesus

BLOSSOM BENNETT

FAITH CHAMBERS WILSON

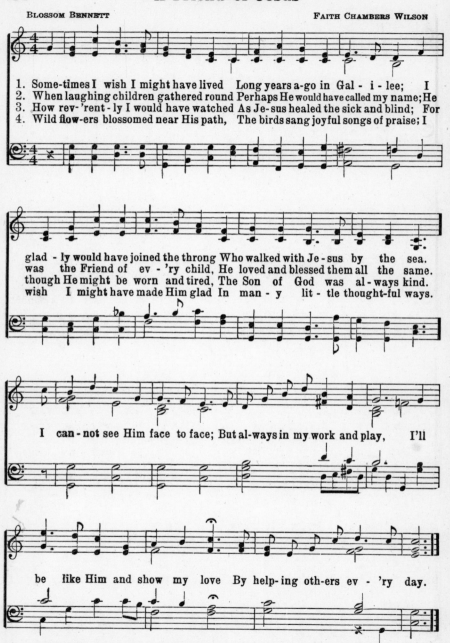

1. Some-times I wish I might have lived Long years a-go in Gal - i - lee; I
2. When laughing children gathered round Perhaps He would have called my name; He
3. How rev-'rent-ly I would have watched As Je-sus healed the sick and blind; For
4. Wild flow-ers blossomed near His path, The birds sang joyful songs of praise; I

glad - ly would have joined the throng Who walked with Je-sus by the sea.
was the Friend of ev - 'ry child, He loved and blessed them all the same.
though He might be worn and tired, The Son of God was al - ways kind.
wish I might have made Him glad In man - y lit - tle thought-ful ways.

I can - not see Him face to face; But al-ways in my work and play, I'll

be like Him and show my love By help-ing oth-ers ev - 'ry day.

Dare to Be a Daniel

P. P. B.

Philip P. Bliss

1. Stand-ing by a pur-pose true, Heed-ing God's com-mand,
2. Man-y might-y men are lost, Dar-ing not to stand,
3. Man-y gi-ants, great and tall, Stalk-ing thro' the land,
4. Hold the Gos-pel ban-ner high! On to vic-tory grand!

Hon-or them, the faith-ful few! All hail to Dan-iel's Band!
Who for God had been a host, By join-ing Dan-iel's Band!
Head-long to the earth would fall, If met by Dan-iel's Band!
Sa-tan and his host de-fy, And shout for Dan-iel's Band!

CHORUS

Dare to be a Dan-iel, Dare to stand a-lone,

Dare to have a pur-pose firm! Dare to make it known!

68   Make Me a Channel of Blessing

H. G. S.

H. G. SMYTH

1. Is your life a chan-nel of bless-ing? Is the love of God
2. Is your life a chan-nel of bless-ing? Are you bur-dened for
3. Is your life a chan-nel of bless-ing? Is it dai - ly
4. We can-not be chan-nels of bless-ing If our lives are not

flow-ing thro' you? Are you tell-ing the lost of the Sav-iour? Are you
those that are lost? Have you urged up-on those who are stray-ing, The
tell-ing for Him? Have you spo-ken the word of sal-va-tion To
free from known sin; We will bar-ri-ers be and a hin-drance To

CHORUS

read-y His serv-ice to do?
Sav-iour who died on the cross?   Make me a chan-nel of bless-ing to-day,
those who are dy-ing in sin?
those we are try-ing to win.

Make me a chan-nel of bless-ing, I pray; My life pos-sess-ing,

my serv-ice bless-ing, Make me a chan-nel of bless-ing to-day.

Marching with the Heroes

WILLIAM G. TARRANT

ADAM GEIBEL

1. March-ing with the he - roes, Com-rades of the strong, Lift we hearts and
2. Glo - ry to the he - roes, Who in days of old Trod the path of
3. So we sing the sto - ry Of the brave and true, Till a - mong the

voic - es As we march a - long; O the joy - ful mu - sic
du - ty, Faith-ful, wise, and bold, For the right un - flinch - ing,
he - roes We are he - roes, too; Loy - al to our Cap - tain

All in cho-rus raise! Theirs the song of tri-umph, Ours the song of praise.
Strong the weak to save, War-riors all and free-men, Fight-ing for the slave.
Like the men of yore, March-ing with the he-roes On-ward, ev - er - more.

REFRAIN

March - ing with the he - roes, Com - rades of the strong,
March-ing, march-ing

Lift we hearts and voic - es As we march a - long.

70   Jesus Never Fails

A. A. L.

A. A. LUTHER
Har. and arr. by CARL BLACKMORE

1. Earth - ly friends may prove un - true, Doubts and fears as - sail;
2. Though the sky be dark and drear, Fierce and strong the gale,
3. In life's dark and bit - ter hour Love will still pre - vail:

One still loves and cares for you: Je - sus nev - er fails.
Just re - mem - ber He is near, And He will not fail.
Trust His ev - er - last - ing pow'r, Je - sus will not fail.

(1.) nev-er fails.

CHORUS

Je - sus nev - er fails, Je - sus nev - er fails;

Heav'n and earth may pass a - way But Je - sus nev - er fails.

Blanche Linthicum and
B. B. McK.

B. B. McKinney

1. Out of James one twen-ty-two Comes a call for Jun-iors true,
2. We would strive for Christ to live; Time and tal-ents we would give;
3. Kind to oth-ers we would be, Je-sus' like-ness they would see;
4. Let us serve with all our might; Let us stand for truth and right,

Who will live for Christ the ris-en Lord: Lis-ten to this trump-et call
We would fol-low Je-sus all the way: Tithes and offerings we would bring;
We would keep our bod-ies clean and strong: We would strive in school and play
Al-ways liv-ing for the ris-en Lord: Come and join our hap-py throng;

Ring-ing out to one and all, "Be ye do-ers of the Word."
We would work and pray and sing For the Mas-ter ev-er-y day.
To learn les-sons and o-bey, Live for right and con-quer wrong.
Sing with us our joy-ous song, "Be ye do-ers of the Word."

CHORUS

"Be ye do-ers of the Word, Be ye do-ers of the Word, Be ye do-ers

of the Word, And not hearers, not hearers on-ly, Be ye do-ers of the Word."

72 More Like the Master

C. H. G.

CHARLES H. GABRIEL

1. More like the Mas-ter I would ev-er be, More of His meek-ness, more hu-mil-i-ty; More zeal to la-bor, more cour-age to be true, More con-se-cra-tion for work He bids me do......Take Thou my heart.....I would be Thine a-lone;.. Take Thou my heart.. and make it all Thine own;.. Purge me from sin.... O Lord, I now im-

2. More like the Mas-ter is my dai-ly prayer; More strength to car-ry cross-es I must bear; More ear-nest ef-fort to bring His king-dom in; More of His Spir-it, the wan-der-er to win........take my heart, I would be Thine a-lone; Take my heart, O take my heart and make it all Thine own; Purge Thou me from ev'ry sin, O Lord, I

3. More like the Mas-ter I would live and grow; More of His love to oth-ers I would show; More self-de-ni-al, like His in Gal-i-lee, More like the Mas-ter I long to ev-er be........Take my heart, O

CHORUS

More Like the Master

plore,.... Wash me and keep.... me Thine for-ev-er-more.
now im-plore, Wash and keep, O wash and keep me Thine for-ev-er-more.

Dare to Be Brave, Dare to Be True   73

W. J. ROOPER

DUNCAN HUME

1. Dare to be brave, dare to be true, Strive for the right, for the
2. Dare to be brave, dare to be true, God is your Fa-ther, He
3. Dare to be brave, dare to be true, God grant you cour-age to

Lord is with you; Fight with sin brave-ly, fight and be strong,
watch-es o'er you; He knows your tri-als; when your heart quails,
car-ry you through; Try to help oth-ers, ev-er be kind,

REFRAIN

Christ is your Cap-tain, fear on-ly what's wrong.
Call Him to res-cue,—His grace nev-er fails. Fight then, good
Let the op-prest a strong friend in you find.

sol-diers, fight and be brave; Christ is your Cap-tain, might-y to save.

74 Loyalty to Christ

E. T. CASSEL

FLORA H. CASSEL

1. From o-ver hill and plain There comes the signal strain, 'Tis loy-al-ty, loy-al-ty,
2. O hear, ye brave, the sound That moves the earth around, 'Tis loy-al-ty, loy-al-ty,
3. Come, join our loy-al throng, We'll rout the gi-ant wrong, 'Tis loy-al-ty, loy-al-ty,
4. The strength of youth we lay At Je-sus' feet to-day, 'Tis loy-al-ty, loy-al-ty,

loy-al-ty, to Christ; Its mus-ic rolls a-long, The hills take up the song,
loy-al-ty, to Christ; A-rise to dare and do, Ring out the watchword true,
loy-al-ty, to Christ; Where Satan's banners float, We'll send the bu-gle note,
loy-al-ty, to Christ; His Gos-pel we'll proclaim, Thro'-out the world's domain,

CHORUS

Of loy-al-ty, loy-al-ty, Yes, loy-al-ty to Christ.
Of loy-al-ty, loy-al-ty, Yes, loy-al-ty to Christ.
Of loy-al-ty, loy-al-ty, Yes, loy-al-ty to Christ. "On to vic-to-ry! On to
Of loy-al-ty, loy-al-ty, Yes, loy-al-ty to Christ.

vic-to-ry!" Cries our great Commander, "On!", . . . We'll move at His command,
great Commander, "On!"

We'll soon possess the land, Thro' loy-al-ty, loy-al-ty, Yes, loy-al-ty to Christ.

Living for Jesus

T. O. CHISHOLM

C. HAROLD LOWDEN

1. Liv-ing for Je-sus   a life that is true, Striv-ing to please Him in all that I   do,
2. Liv-ing for Je-sus who died in my place, Bear-ing on Cal-v'ry my sin and dis-grace,
3. Liv-ing for Je-sus wher-ev - er   I   am,   Do - ing each du-ty   in His ho - ly name,
4. Liv-ing for Je-sus thro' earth's lit-tle while, My dear-est treas-ure, the light of His smile,

Yield-ing al-le-giance, glad-heart-ed and free, This is   the path-way of bless-ing for me.
Such love.constrains me to an-swer His call, Fol-low His lead-ing and give Him my all.
Will - ing to suf - fer af - flic-tion or loss, Deem-ing each tri-al   a part of   my cross.
Seek-ing the lost ones He died to   re-deem, Bring-ing the wea-ry   to find rest in Him.

CHORUS

O Je-sus, Lord and Sav-iour, I give my-self to Thee;   For Thou, in Thy a-

tone-ment, Didst give Thy-self for   me;   I own no oth - er Mas - ter,   My

heart shall be Thy throne, My life I give, henceforth to live, O Christ, for Thee a - lone.

Yield Not to Temptation

H. R. P.

H. R. PALMER

1. Yield not to temp-ta - tion, For yield-ing is sin; Each vic-tory will
2. Shun e - vil com-pan-ions, Bad lan-guage dis-dain; God's name hold in
3. To him that o'er-com-eth, God giv-eth a crown; Thro' faith we will

help you Some oth - er to win; Fight man - ful - ly on - ward,
rev-erence, Nor take it in vain; Be thought-ful and ear - nest,
con - quer, Though of-ten cast down; He who is our Sav - iour,

Dark pas-sions sub - due; Look ev - er to Je - sus, He'll car-ry you through.
Kind-heart-ed and true; Look ev - er to Je - sus, He'll car-ry you through.
Our strength will re-new; Look ev - er to Je - sus, He'll car-ry you through.

CHORUS

Ask the Sav - iour to help you, Com - fort, strength-en, and keep you;

He is will-ing to aid you, He will car-ry you through.

Trust, Try, and Prove Me

L. S. L.

LIDA SHIVERS LEECH

1. Bring ye all the tithes in - to the store-house, All your mon - ey,
2. When my wa-vering faith in tri - als fal - ter, When His guid-ing
3. I have yield - ed Him my life for - ev - er, All I am, or

tal - ents, time and love; Con - se-crate them all up - on the
hand I can - not see, Then in won-drous love and ten - der
have, or hope to be; Naught on earth my hold on Him can

al - tar; While your Sav - iour from a - bove speaks sweet - ly,
mer - cy, Through His Word He says to me, My child, just
sev - er, While I hear Him say to me, My child, just

REFRAIN

Trust Me, try Me, prove Me, saith the Lord of hosts, and see
Trust Me, yes, then try Me, prove Me,

If a bless-ing, un-meas-ured bless-ing, I will not pour out on thee.

78 True-Hearted, Whole-Hearted

FRANCES R. HAVERGAL

GEORGE C. STEBBINS

1. True-hearted, whole-hearted, faith-ful and loy-al, King of our lives, by Thy grace we will be; Un-der the standard ex-alt-ed and roy-al, Strong in Thy strength we will bat-tle for Thee.

2. True-hearted, whole-hearted, full-est al-le-giance Yielding henceforth to our glo-ri-ous King; Val-iant en-deav-or and lov-ing o-be-dience, Free-ly and joy-ous-ly now would we bring.

3. True-hearted, whole-hearted, Sav-iour all-glo-rious! Take Thy great pow-er and reign there a-lone, O-ver our wills and af-fec-tions vic-to-rious, Free-ly sur-ren-dered and whol-ly Thine own.

CHORUS

Peal out the watch-word! si-lence it nev-er! Song of our spir-its, re-joic-ing and free; Peal out the watch-word! loy-al for-ev-er, King of our lives, by Thy grace we will be.

Our Best

S. C. KIRK

GRANT COLFAX TULLAR

1. Hear ye the Mas-ter's call, "Give Me thy best!" For, be it great or small,
2. Wait not for men to laud, Heed not their slight; Win-ning the smile of God

That is His test. Do then the best you can, Not for re-ward, Not for the
Brings its de-light! Aid-ing the good and true Ne'er goes un-blest, All that we

CHORUS.

praise of man, But for the Lord.
think or do, Be it the best. Ev - 'ry work for Je - sus will be blest,

But He asks from ev-'ry - one His best. Our tal-ents may be few,

These may be small, But un - to Him is due Our best, our all.

80 My Desire

J. P. S.

J. P. SCHOLFIELD

1. I want my life to glo-ri-fy my Lord and King; I want to please and
2. Oh, that my life might magnify the Sav-iour's pow'r; Oh, that my deeds might
3. I want my life to tes-ti-fy that He can save; I want to help to

hon-or Him in ev-'ry-thing; I want my life to tell men that He is my
wit-ness to His grace each hour; Oh, that my words might magnify His ho-ly
make His crimson ban-ner wave; I want to tell the bless-ed sto-ry ev-'ry

CHORUS

Guide; I want the world to know He's walking by my side.
name, So let my heart and voice His mighty pow'r proclaim. I want to live as
day; I want to be a light to oth-ers on their way.

Je-sus lived, I want to love as Je-sus loved, I want to serve and honor Him and

please Him in ev-'ry-thing; I want my life to test-ti-fy that He's my Lord and King.

Serve the Lord with Gladness

B. B. McK. B. B. McKinney

1. "Serve the Lord with gladness" In our works and ways, Come be-fore His pres-ence
2. "Serve the Lord with gladness," Thankful all the while For His ten-der mer-cies,
3. "Serve the Lord with gladness," This shall be our theme, As we walk to-geth-er

With our songs of praise; Un-to Him our Mak-er We would pledge anew (a-new),
For His lov-ing smile. Bless-ed truth en-dur-ing, Always just the same (the same),
In His love su-preme. Listening, ev-er lis-tening, For the still small voice (His voice),

Chorus

Life's supreme de-vo-tion To serv-ice true.
We will serve with gladness And praise His name. "Serve Him with gladness," Enter His courts with
His sweet will so precious Will be our choice.

song (with song); To our Cre-a-tor True praises be-long (belong). Great is His mer-cy,

Won-der-ful is His name (His name), We glad-ly serve Him, His great love proclaim (proclaim).

The Fight Is On

Mrs. C. H. M.

Mrs. C. H. Morris

1. The fight is on, the trump-et sound is ring-ing out, The cry "To
2. The fight is on, a-rouse, ye sol-diers brave and true! Je-ho-vah
3. The Lord is lead-ing on to cer-tain vic-to-ry; The bow of

arms!" is heard a-far and near; The Lord of hosts is march-ing on to
leads, and vic-tory will as-sure; Go buck-le on the ar-mor God has
prom-ise spans the east-ern sky; His glo-rious name in ev-ery land shall

vic-to-ry, The tri-umph of the Christ will soon ap-pear.
giv-en you, And in His strength un-to the end en-dure.
hon-ored be; The morn will break, the dawn of peace is nigh.

Chorus

The fight is on, O Chris-tian sol-dier, And face to face in stern ar-ray, With

ar-mor gleaming, and col-ors streaming, The right and wrong engage to-day!

The Fight Is On

The fight is on, but be not wea - ry; Be strong and in His might hold fast;

If God be for us, His ban-ner o'er us, We'll sing the victor's song at last!
Vic-tory! Vic-tory!

Let the Beauty of Jesus

83

ALBERT OSBORN

W. HINES SIMS

Unison Chorus

Let the beau-ty of Je-sus be seen in me, All His

won-der-ful pas-sion and pu - ri - ty; O Thou spir - it di - vine,

All my na-ture re-fine, Till the beau-ty of Je-sus be seen in me.

Building, Daily Building

Flora Kirkland

I. H. Meredith

1. Build — ing, dai-ly build — ing,
2. Choos — ing, as we la — bor,
3. May...... the Lord ap-prove us!

While........ the mo-ments fly,............ We............ are ev — er
What........ we wish to take,........ Oh,........... let us be
'Tis............ our earn - est pray'r, ... Oh,........... to have our

build — ing Life - - work for on high!........
care — ful For............. our Mas — ter's sake!........
build — ing Tall,.......... and strong and fair!...........

Char — ac-ter we're build — ing, Thoughts and ac-tions free.......
He.........will help our la — bor He.......... will strength bestow; ..
Oh,.........to live for Je — sus! Tru — ly ev-'ry hour,......

Make........ for us a build — ing For......... e- ter- ni - ty.......
Let............ us choose for Je — sus, All......... we use be - low......
Build — -ing, praying, trust — ing In......... His mighty pow'r!..

Building, Daily Building

CHORUS

We are building day by day, While the mo-ments pass a-way, We are build-ing, ev-er build-ing; We are build-ing day by day, While the mo-ments pass a-way, We are build-ing for e-ter-ni-ty.

Saviour, Teach Me, Day by Day

85

JANE E. LEESON

CARL M. VON WEBER

1. Sav-iour, teach me day by day, Love's sweet les-son to o-bey;
2. With a child-like heart of love, At Thy bid-ding may I move;
3. Teach me all Thy steps to trace, Strong to fol-low in Thy grace;
4. Love in lov-ing finds em-ploy, In o-be-dience all her joy;

Sweet-er les-son can-not be— Lov-ing Him who first loved me.
Prompt to serve and fol-low Thee—Lov-ing Him who first loved me.
Learn-ing how to love from Thee—Lov-ing Him who first loved me.
Ev-er new that joy will be— Lov-ing Him who first loved me.

Tell Me the Stories of Jesus

W. H. PARKER

F. A. CHALLINOR

1. Tell me the sto-ries of Je-sus I love to hear;
2. First let me hear how the chil-dren Stood round his knee;
3. In-to the cit-y I'd fol-low The chil-dren's band,
4. Tell me, in ac-cents of won-der, How rolled the sea,

Things I would ask Him to tell me If He were here; Scenes by the way-side,
And I shall fan-cy his bless-ing Rest-ing on me: Words full of kind-ness,
Wav-ing a branch of the palm-tree High in my hand; One of his her-alds,
Toss-ing the boat in a tem-pest On Gal-i-lee! And how the Mas-ter,

Tales of the sea, Sto-ries of Je-sus, Tell them to me.
Deeds full of grace, All in the love-light Of Je-sus' face.
Yes, I would sing Loud-est ho-san-nas! Je-sus is King!
Read-y and kind, Chid-ed the bil-lows, And hushed the wind.

87

O Master, Let Me Walk with Thee

W. GLADDEN

H. P. SMITH

1. O Mas-ter, let me walk with Thee In low-ly paths of serv-ice free;
2. Help me the slow of heart to move By some clear, win-ning word of love;
3. Teach me Thy patience! still with Thee In clos-er, dear-er com-pa-ny,
4. In hope that sends a shin-ing ray Far down the future's broadening way,

O Master, Let Me Walk with Thee

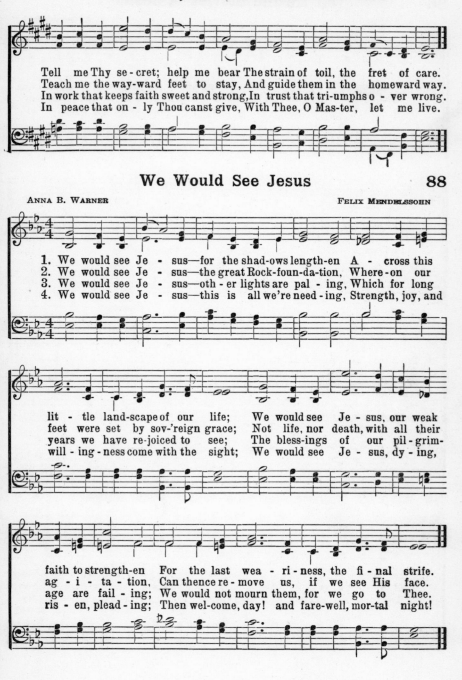

Tell me Thy se - cret; help me bear The strain of toil, the fret of care.
Teach me the way-ward feet to stay, And guide them in the homeward way.
In work that keeps faith sweet and strong, In trust that tri-umphs o - ver wrong.
In peace that on - ly Thou canst give, With Thee, O Mas-ter, let me live.

We Would See Jesus   88

ANNA B. WARNER

FELIX MENDELSSOHN

1. We would see Je - sus—for the shad-ows length-en A - cross this
2. We would see Je - sus—the great Rock-foun-da-tion, Where-on our
3. We would see Je - sus—oth - er lights are pal - ing, Which for long
4. We would see Je - sus—this is all we're need-ing, Strength, joy, and

lit - tle land-scape of our life; We would see Je - sus, our weak
feet were set by sov'reign grace; Not life, nor death, with all their
years we have re-joiced to see; The bless-ings of our pil - grim-
will - ing - ness come with the sight; We would see Je - sus, dy - ing,

faith to strength-en For the last wea - ri - ness, the fi - nal strife.
ag - i - ta - tion, Can thence re - move us, if we see His face.
age are fail - ing; We would not mourn them, for we go to Thee.
ris - en, plead - ing; Then wel-come, day! and fare-well, mor-tal night!

Heavenly Sunlight

H. J. ZELLEY   G. H. COOK

1. Walk-ing in sun-light, all of my jour-ney; O - ver the moun-tains,
2. Shad-ows a - round me, shad-ows a - bove me, Nev-er con - ceal my
3. In the bright sun-light, ev - er re - joic-ing, Press-ing my way to

thro' the deep vale; Je - sus has said "I'll nev - er for - sake thee,"
Sav - iour and Guide; He is the light, in Him is no dark - ness;
man-sions a - bove; Sing-ing His prais - es glad - ly I'm walk - ing,

CHORUS

Prom-ise di - vine that nev - er can fail.
Ev - er I'm walk - ing close to His side. Heav-en - ly sun - light,
Walk-ing in sun - light, sun-light of love.

heav-en - ly sun - light, Flood-ing my soul with glo - ry di - vine: Hal-le

lu - jah, I am re - joic - ing, Sing-ing His prais-es, Je - sus is mine.

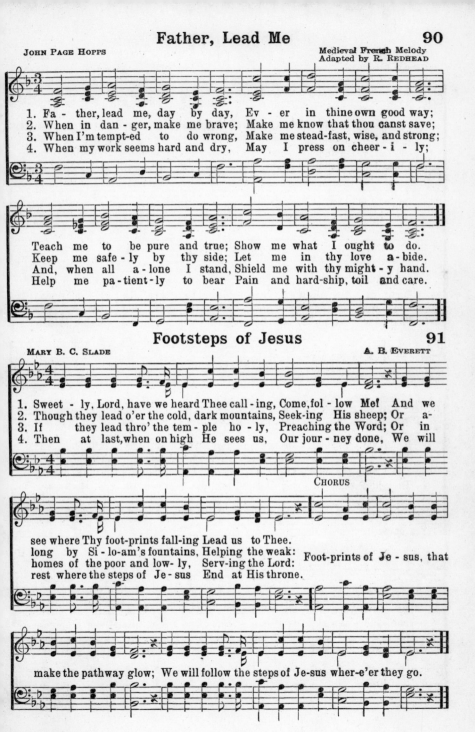

Father, Lead Me

JOHN PAGE HOPPS

Medieval French Melody
Adapted by R. REDHEAD

1. Fa - ther, lead me, day by day, Ev - er in thine own good way;
2. When in dan - ger, make me brave; Make me know that thou canst save;
3. When I'm tempt-ed to do wrong, Make me stead-fast, wise, and strong;
4. When my work seems hard and dry, May I press on cheer - i - ly;

Teach me to be pure and true; Show me what I ought to do.
Keep me safe - ly by thy side; Let me in thy love a - bide.
And, when all a - lone I stand, Shield me with thy might - y hand.
Help me pa - tient - ly to bear Pain and hard-ship, toil and care.

Footsteps of Jesus

MARY B. C. SLADE

A. B. EVERETT

1. Sweet - ly, Lord, have we heard Thee call - ing, Come, fol - low Me! And we
2. Though they lead o'er the cold, dark mountains, Seek - ing His sheep; Or a -
3. If they lead thro' the tem - ple ho - ly, Preaching the Word; Or in
4. Then at last, when on high He sees us, Our jour - ney done, We will

CHORUS

see where Thy foot-prints fall-ing Lead us to Thee.
long by Si - lo-am's fountains, Helping the weak: Foot-prints of Je - sus, that
homes of the poor and low- ly, Serv-ing the Lord:
rest where the steps of Je - sus End at His throne.

make the pathway glow; We will follow the steps of Je-sus wher-e'er they go.

Stand Up, Stand Up for Jesus

GEORGE DUFFIELD

GEORGE J. WEBB

1. Stand up, stand up for Je - sus, Ye sol - diers of the cross!
2. Stand up, stand up for Je - sus, The trump - et call o - bey;
3. Stand up, stand up for Je - sus, Stand in His strength a - lone;
4. Stand up, stand up for Je - sus, The strife will not be long;

Lift high His roy - al ban - ner, It must not suf - fer loss:
Forth to the might - y con - flict, In this His glo - rious day:
The arm of flesh will fail you, Ye dare not trust your own:
This day, the noise of bat - tle, The next, the vic - tor's song:

From vic - tory un - to vic - tory, His ar - my shall He lead,
Ye that are men, now serve Him, A - gainst un - num-bered foes;
Put on the gos - pel ar - mor, And, watch-ing un - to prayer,
To him that o - ver - com - eth, A crown of life shall be;

Till ev - ery foe is van-quished And Christ is Lord in - deed.
Your cour - age rise with dan - ger, And strength to strength op-pose.
Where du - ty calls, or dan - ger, Be nev - er want - ing there.
He with the King of Glo - ry Shall reign e - ter - nal - ly!

Priscilla J. Owens

William J. Kirkpatrick

1. We have heard the joy - ful sound: Je - sus saves! Je - sus saves!
2. Waft it on the roll - ing tide; Je - sus saves! Je - sus saves!
3. Sing a - bove the bat - tle strife, Je - sus saves! Je - sus saves!
4. Give the winds a might - y voice, Je - sus saves! Je - sus saves!

Spread the ti - dings all a - round: Je - sus saves! Je - sus saves!
Tell to sin - ners far and wide: Je - sus saves! Je - sus saves!
By His death and end - less life, Je - sus saves! Je - sus saves!
Let the na - tions now re - joice,— Je - sus saves! Je - sus saves!

Bear the news to ev - er - y land, Climb the steeps and cross the waves;
Sing, ye is - lands of the sea; Ech - o back, ye o - cean caves;
Sing it soft - ly through the gloom, When the heart for mer - cy craves;
Shout sal - va - tion full and free; High - est hills and deep - est caves;

On - ward!—'tis our Lord's com - mand; Je - sus saves! Je - sus saves!
Earth shall keep her ju - bi - lee: Je - sus saves! Je - sus saves!
Sing in tri - umph o'er the tomb,— Je - sus saves! Je - sus saves!
This our song of vic - to - ry,— Je - sus saves! Je - sus saves!

I Am Thine, O Lord

FANNY J. CROSBY

W. H. DOANE

1. I am Thine, O Lord, I have heard Thy voice, And it told Thy
2. Con-se-crate me now to Thy serv-ice, Lord, By the power of
3. O the pure de-light of a sin-gle hour That be-fore Thy
4. There are depths of love that I can-not know Till I cross the

love to me; But I long to rise in the arms of faith, And be
grace di-vine; Let my soul look up with a stead-fast hope, And my
throne I spend, When I kneel in prayer, and with Thee, my God, I com-
nar-row sea; There are heights of joy that I may not reach Till I

clos-er drawn to Thee.
will be lost in Thine. Draw me near-er, near-er, bless-ed
mune as friend with friend!
rest in peace with Thee.

near-er, near-er,

Lord, To the cross where Thou hast died; Draw me near-er, near-er,

near-er, bless-ed Lord, To Thy pre-cious, bleed-ing side.

Jesus Is Calling

FANNY J. CROSBY

GEORGE C. STEBBINS

1. Je - sus is ten - der - ly call - ing thee home— Call - ing to - day,
2. Je - sus is call - ing the wea - ry to rest— Call - ing to - day,
3. Je - sus is wait - ing; O come to Him now— Wait - ing to - day,
4. Je - sus is plead - ing; O list to His voice: Hear Him to - day,

call - ing to - day; Why from the sun - shine of love wilt thou roam
call - ing to - day; Bring Him thy bur - den and thou shalt be blest;
wait - ing to - day; Come with thy sins; at His feet low - ly bow;
hear Him to - day; They who be - lieve on His name shall re - joice;

REFRAIN

Far - ther and far - ther a - way?
He will not turn thee a - way.
Come, and no lon - ger de - lay.
Quick - ly a - rise and a - way.

Call - - ing to - day, ...
Call - ing, call - ing to - day, to - day,

Call - - ing to - day, ...
Call - ing, call - ing to - day, to - day;

Je - - - - sus is
Je - sus is ten - der - ly

call - - - - ing, Is ten - der - ly call - ing to - day.
call - ing to - day,

Take the Name of Jesus with You

Mrs. Lydia Baxter

W. H. Doane

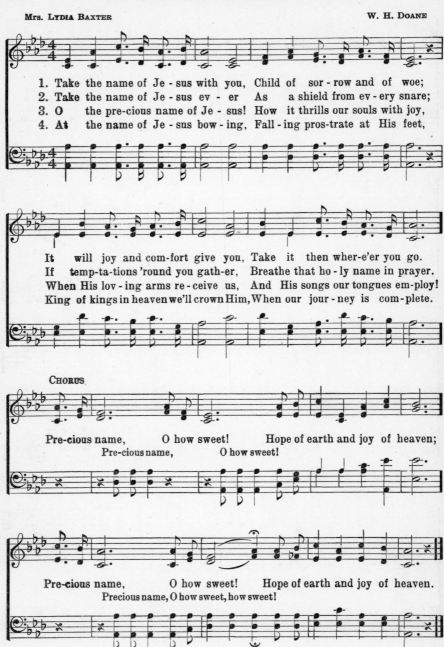

1. Take the name of Je - sus with you, Child of sor - row and of woe;
2. Take the name of Je - sus ev - er As a shield from ev - ery snare;
3. O the pre - cious name of Je - sus! How it thrills our souls with joy,
4. At the name of Je - sus bow - ing, Fall - ing pros - trate at His feet,

It will joy and com - fort give you, Take it then wher - e'er you go.
If temp - ta - tions 'round you gath - er, Breathe that ho - ly name in prayer.
When His lov - ing arms re - ceive us, And His songs our tongues em - ploy!
King of kings in heaven we'll crown Him, When our jour - ney is com - plete.

Chorus

Pre - cious name, O how sweet! Hope of earth and joy of heaven;
Pre - cious name, O how sweet!

Pre - cious name, O how sweet! Hope of earth and joy of heaven.
Precious name, O how sweet, how sweet!

Lord, I Want to Be a Christian

Negro Spiritual

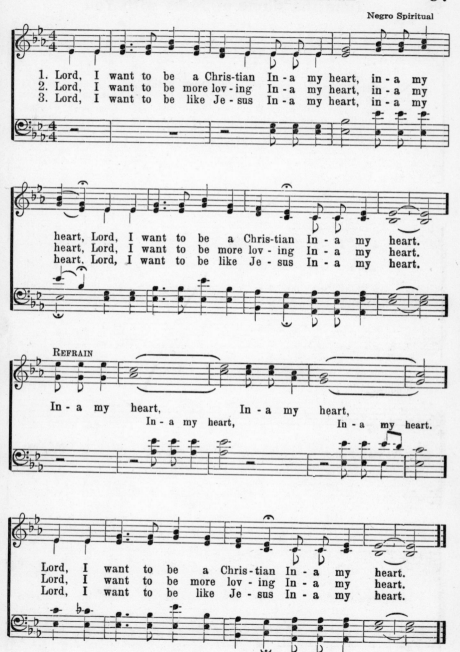

1. Lord, I want to be a Chris-tian In-a my heart, in-a my
2. Lord, I want to be more lov-ing In-a my heart, in-a my
3. Lord, I want to be like Je-sus In-a my heart, in-a my

heart, Lord, I want to be a Chris-tian In-a my heart.
heart, Lord, I want to be more lov-ing In-a my heart.
heart, Lord, I want to be like Je-sus In-a my heart.

REFRAIN

In-a my heart, In-a my heart,
In-a my heart, In-a my heart.

Lord, I want to be a Chris-tian In-a my heart.
Lord, I want to be more lov-ing In-a my heart.
Lord, I want to be like Je-sus In-a my heart.

Trusting Jesus

98

E. PAGE

IRA D. SANKEY

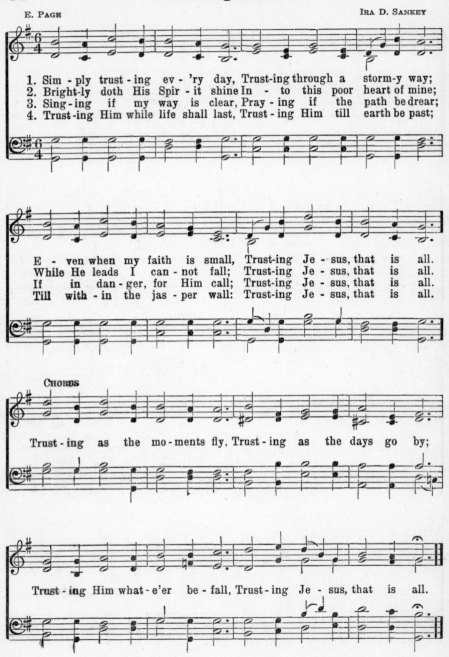

1. Sim - ply trust - ing ev - 'ry day, Trust - ing through a storm-y way;
2. Bright-ly doth His Spir - it shine In - to this poor heart of mine;
3. Sing - ing if my way is clear, Pray - ing if the path be drear;
4. Trust - ing Him while life shall last, Trust - ing Him till earth be past;

E - ven when my faith is small, Trust-ing Je - sus, that is all.
While He leads I can - not fall; Trust-ing Je - sus, that is all.
If in dan - ger, for Him call; Trust-ing Je - sus, that is all.
Till with - in the jas - per wall: Trust-ing Je - sus, that is all.

CHORUS

Trust - ing as the mo - ments fly, Trust - ing as the days go by;

Trust - ing Him what - e'er be - fall, Trust - ing Je - sus, that is all.

'Tis So Sweet to Trust in Jesus

Louisa M. R. Stead

William J. Kirkpatrick

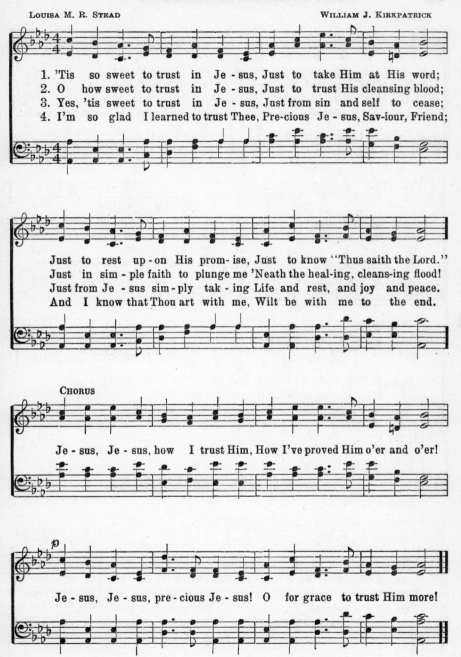

1. 'Tis so sweet to trust in Je-sus, Just to take Him at His word;
2. O how sweet to trust in Je-sus, Just to trust His cleansing blood;
3. Yes, 'tis sweet to trust in Je-sus, Just from sin and self to cease;
4. I'm so glad I learned to trust Thee, Pre-cious Je-sus, Sav-iour, Friend;

Just to rest up-on His prom-ise, Just to know "Thus saith the Lord."
Just in sim-ple faith to plunge me 'Neath the heal-ing, cleans-ing flood!
Just from Je-sus sim-ply tak-ing Life and rest, and joy and peace.
And I know that Thou art with me, Wilt be with me to the end.

CHORUS

Je-sus, Je-sus, how I trust Him, How I've proved Him o'er and o'er!

Je-sus, Je-sus, pre-cious Je-sus! O for grace to trust Him more!

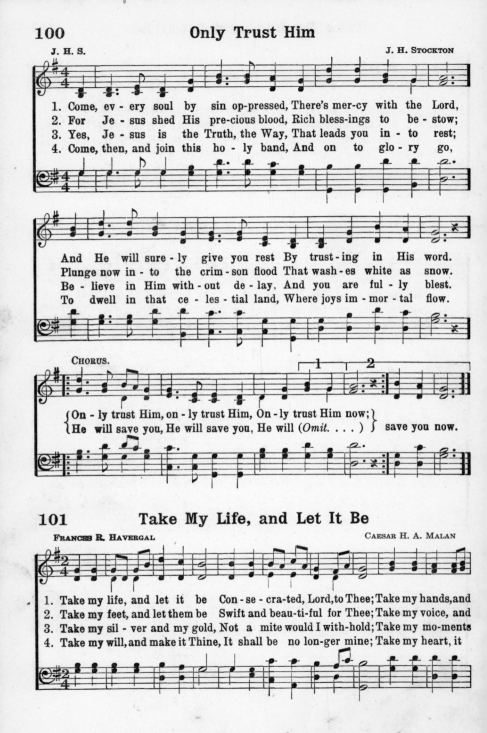

100 Only Trust Him

J. H. S.   J. H. STOCKTON

1. Come, ev - ery soul by sin op-pressed, There's mer-cy with the Lord,
2. For Je - sus shed His pre-cious blood, Rich bless-ings to be - stow;
3. Yes, Je - sus is the Truth, the Way, That leads you in - to rest;
4. Come, then, and join this ho - ly band, And on to glo - ry go,

And He will sure - ly give you rest By trust-ing in His word.
Plunge now in - to the crim - son flood That wash - es white as snow.
Be - lieve in Him with - out de - lay, And you are ful - ly blest.
To dwell in that ce - les - tial land, Where joys im - mor - tal flow.

CHORUS.

{On - ly trust Him, on - ly trust Him, On - ly trust Him now;}
{He will save you, He will save you, He will (*Omit*. . . .) } save you now.

101 Take My Life, and Let It Be

FRANCES R. HAVERGAL   CAESAR H. A. MALAN

1. Take my life, and let it be Con - se - cra-ted, Lord, to Thee; Take my hands, and
2. Take my feet, and let them be Swift and beau-ti-ful for Thee; Take my voice, and
3. Take my sil - ver and my gold, Not a mite would I with-hold; Take my mo-ments
4. Take my will, and make it Thine, It shall be no lon-ger mine; Take my heart, it

Take My Life, and Let It Be

let them move At the im-pulse of Thy love, At the im-pulse of Thy love.
let me sing, Al-ways, on-ly, for my King, Al-ways, on-ly, for my King.
and my days, Let them flow in ceaseless praise, Let them flow in ceaseless praise.
is Thine own; It shall be Thy roy-al throne, It shall be Thy roy-al throne.

I Am Coming, Lord

102

L. H.

LOUIS HARTSOUGH

1. I hear Thy welcome voice, That calls me, Lord, to Thee, For cleansing
2. Tho' com-ing weak and vile, Thou dost my strength assure; Thou dost my
3. 'Tis Je-sus calls me on To per-fect faith and love, To per-fect

CHORUS

in Thy pre-cious blood That flowed on Cal-va-ry.
vile-ness ful-ly cleanse, Till spot-less all and pure.   I am com-ing, Lord!
hope, and peace, and trust, For earth and heaven a-bove.

Coming now to Thee! Wash me, cleanse me in the blood That flowed on Cal-va-ry!

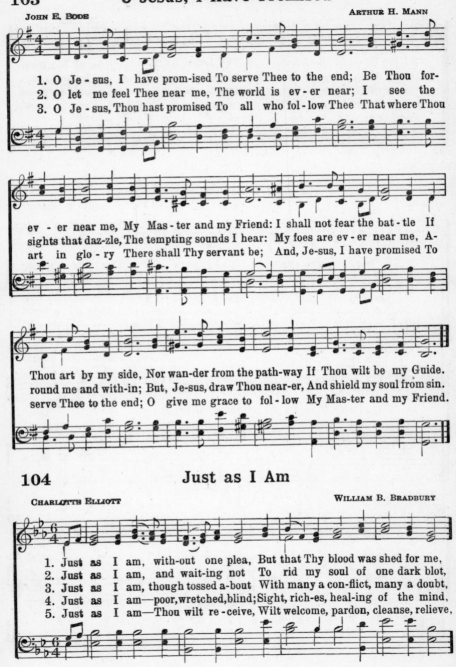

103 O Jesus, I Have Promised

JOHN E. BODE

ARTHUR H. MANN

1. O Je-sus, I have prom-ised To serve Thee to the end; Be Thou for-ev-er near me, My Mas-ter and my Friend: I shall not fear the bat-tle If Thou art by my side, Nor wan-der from the path-way If Thou wilt be my Guide.

2. O let me feel Thee near me, The world is ev-er near; I see the sights that daz-zle, The tempting sounds I hear: My foes are ev-er near me, A-round me and with-in; But, Je-sus, draw Thou near-er, And shield my soul from sin.

3. O Je-sus, Thou hast promised To all who fol-low Thee That where Thou art in glo-ry There shall Thy servant be; And, Je-sus, I have promised To serve Thee to the end; O give me grace to fol-low My Mas-ter and my Friend.

104 Just as I Am

CHARLOTTE ELLIOTT

WILLIAM B. BRADBURY

1. Just as I am, with-out one plea, But that Thy blood was shed for me,

2. Just as I am, and wait-ing not To rid my soul of one dark blot,

3. Just as I am, though tossed a-bout With many a con-flict, many a doubt,

4. Just as I am—poor, wretched, blind; Sight, rich-es, heal-ing of the mind,

5. Just as I am—Thou wilt re-ceive, Wilt welcome, pardon, cleanse, relieve,

Just as I Am

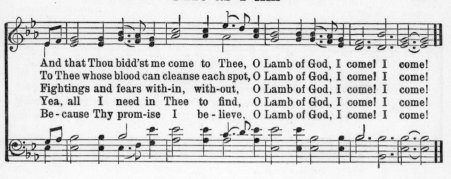

And that Thou bidd'st me come to Thee, O Lamb of God, I come! I come!
To Thee whose blood can cleanse each spot, O Lamb of God, I come! I come!
Fightings and fears with-in, with-out, O Lamb of God, I come! I come!
Yea, all I need in Thee to find, O Lamb of God, I come! I come!
Be-cause Thy prom-ise I be-lieve, O Lamb of God, I come! I come!

O Happy Day

105

PHILIP DODDRIDGE

EDWARD F. RIMBAULT

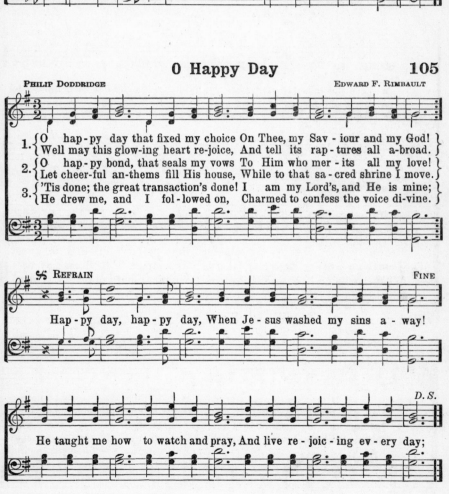

1. {O hap-py day that fixed my choice On Thee, my Sav-iour and my God! }
   {Well may this glow-ing heart re-joice, And tell its rap-tures all a-broad. }

2. {O hap-py bond, that seals my vows To Him who mer-its all my love! }
   {Let cheer-ful an-thems fill His house, While to that sa-cred shrine I move. }

3. {'Tis done; the great transaction's done! I am my Lord's, and He is mine; }
   {He drew me, and I fol-lowed on, Charmed to confess the voice di-vine. }

REFRAIN

FINE

Hap-py day, hap-py day, When Je-sus washed my sins a-way!

D. S.

He taught me how to watch and pray, And live re-joic-ing ev-ery day;

106 All the Way My Saviour Leads Me

FANNY J. CROSBY   ROBERT LOWRY

1. All the way my Sav-iour leads me; What have I to ask be-side?
2. All the way my Sav-iour leads me, Cheers each wind-ing path I tread,
3. All the way my Sav-iour leads me; Oh, the full-ness of His love!

Can I doubt His ten-der mer-cy, Who through life has been my Guide?
Gives me grace for ev-ery tri-al, Feeds me with the liv-ing bread.
Per-fect rest to me is prom-ised In my Fa-ther's house a-bove.

Heaven-ly peace, di-vin-est com-fort, Here by faith in Him to dwell!
Though my wea-ry steps may fal-ter, And my soul a-thirst may be,
When my spir-it, clothed im-mor-tal, Wings its flight to realms of day,

For I know, what-e'er be-fall me, Je-sus do-eth all things well; well.
Gushing from the Rock be-fore me, Lo! a spring of joy I see; see.
This my song thro' end-less a-ges: Je-sus led me all the way; way.

What a Friend

JOSEPH SCRIVEN

CHARLES C. CONVERSE

1. What a Friend we have in Je - sus, All our sins and griefs to bear!
2. Have we tri - als and temp-ta - tions? Is there trou-ble an - y-where?
3. Are we weak and heav-y - la - den, Cum-bered with a load of care?

What a priv - i - lege to car - ry Ev - 'ry-thing to God in prayer!
We should ne - ver be dis-cour - aged, Take it to the Lord in prayer.
Pre - cious Sav -iour, still our ref - uge,— Take it to the Lord in prayer.

O what peace we of - ten for - feit, O what need-less pain we bear,
Can we find a friend so faith - ful Who will all our sor -rows share?
Do thy friends de-spise, for-sake thee? Take it to the Lord in prayer;

All be-cause we do not car - ry Ev - 'ry-thing to God in prayer!
Je - sus knows our ev - 'ry weak-ness, Take it to the Lord in prayer.
In His arms He'll take and shield thee, Thou wilt find a sol-ace there.

108 Jesus Loves Even Me

P. P. B.

PHILIP P. BLISS

1. I am so glad that our Fa-ther in heaven Tells of His love in the Book He has given; Won-der-ful things in the Bi-ble I see: This is the dear-est, that Je-sus loves me.

2. Tho' I for-get Him and wan-der a-way, Still He doth love me wher-ev-er I stray; Back to His dear lov-ing arms would I flee, When I re-mem-ber that Je-sus loves me.

3. Oh, if there's on-ly one song I can sing, When in His beau-ty I see the great King, This shall my song in e-ter-ni-ty be: "Oh, what a won-der that Je-sus loves me."

CHORUS

I am so glad that Je-sus loves me, Je-sus loves me, Je-sus loves me, I am so glad that Je-sus loves me, Je-sus loves e-ven me.

The Sweet Story of Old

109

Mrs. Jemima Luke

J. C. Englebrecht

1. I think when I read that sweet sto-ry of old When Je-sus was here
2. I wish that His hands had been placed on my head, That His arm had been thrown
3. Yet still to His foot-stool in prayer I may go, And ask for a share
4. In that beau-ti-ful place He is gone to pre-pare, For all that are washed

a-mong men, How He called lit-tle chil-dren as lambs to His fold, I should
a-round me; And that I might have seen His kind look when he said "Let the
in His love; And if I now ear-nest-ly seek Him be-low, I shall
and for-giv'n; And man-y dear chil-dren are gath-er-ing there, For "Of

FINE   REFRAIN   D. S.

like to have been with them then. I should like to have been with them then.
lit-tle ones come un-to Me;" "Let the lit-tle ones come un-to Me."
see Him and hear Him a-bove. I shall see Him and hear Him a-bove.
such is the king-dom of heaven" For "Of such is the king-dom of heaven."

Teach Me to Do Thy Will

110

Psalm 143: 10

Faith Chambers Wilson

Teach me, O Lord, to do Thy will, Teach me to do Thy will. For

Thou art my God; Thy Spir-it is good: Lead me un-to the land of up-rightness.

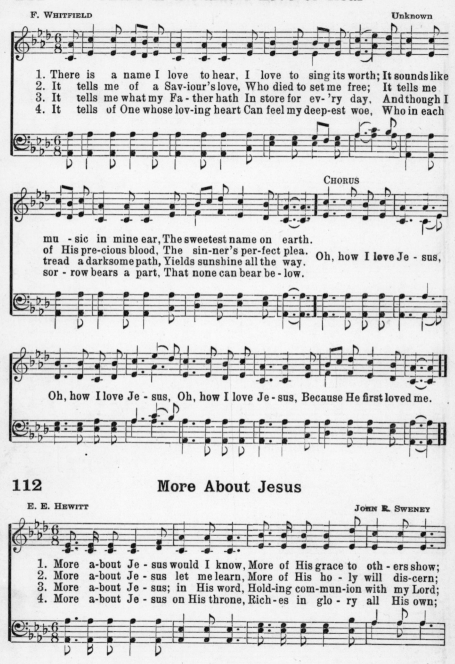

111 There Is a Name I Love to Hear

F. WHITFIELD

Unknown

1. There is a name I love to hear, I love to sing its worth; It sounds like
2. It tells me of a Sav-iour's love, Who died to set me free; It tells me
3. It tells me what my Fa-ther hath In store for ev-'ry day, And though I
4. It tells of One whose lov-ing heart Can feel my deep-est woe, Who in each

CHORUS

mu-sic in mine ear, The sweetest name on earth.
of His pre-cious blood, The sin-ner's per-fect plea.
tread a darksome path, Yields sunshine all the way. Oh, how I love Je - sus,
sor-row bears a part, That none can bear be-low.

Oh, how I love Je - sus, Oh, how I love Je - sus, Because He first loved me.

112 More About Jesus

E. E. HEWITT

JOHN R. SWENEY

1. More a-bout Je - sus would I know, More of His grace to oth - ers show;
2. More a-bout Je - sus let me learn, More of His ho - ly will dis-cern;
3. More a-bout Je - sus; in His word, Hold-ing com-mun-ion with my Lord;
4. More a-bout Je - sus on His throne, Rich-es in glo - ry all His own;

More About Jesus

More of His sav - ing full - ness see, More of His love who died for me.
Spir - it of God, my teach - er be, Show - ing the things of Christ to me.
Hear - ing His voice in ev - 'ry line, Mak - ing each faith - ful say - ing mine.
More of His kingdom's sure in - crease; More of His com - ing, Prince of Peace.

D. S.—*More of His sav - ing full - ness see, More of His love who died for me.*

REFRAIN

More, more a - bout Je - sus, More, more a - bout Je - sus;

I Need Thee Every Hour   113

MRS. ANNIE S. HAWKS

ROBERT LOWRY

1. I need Thee ev - 'ry hour, Most gra - cious Lord; No ten - der voice like
2. I need Thee ev - 'ry hour, Stay Thou near by; Temp - ta - tions lose their
3. I need Thee ev - 'ry hour, In joy or pain; Come quick - ly and a -
4. I need Thee ev - 'ry hour, Most Ho - ly One; O make me Thine in -

CHORUS

Thine Can peace af - ford.
power When Thou art nigh.   I need Thee, O, I need Thee; Ev - 'ry hour I
bide, Or life is vain.
deed, Thou bless - ed Son.

need Thee! O bless me now, my Sav - iour, I come to Thee!

114 I've Found a Friend

J. G. SMALL

GEORGE C. STEBBINS

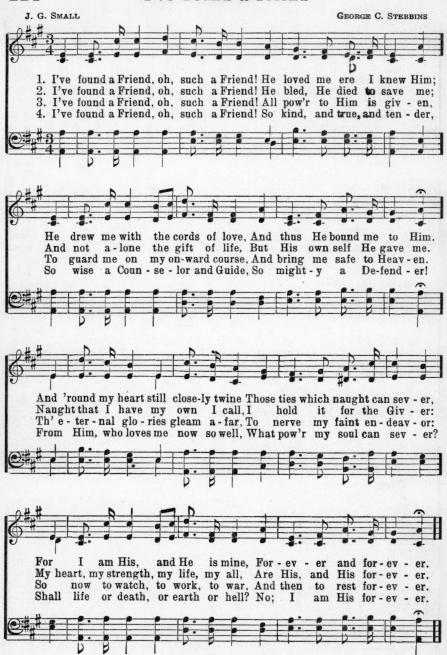

1. I've found a Friend, oh, such a Friend! He loved me ere I knew Him;
2. I've found a Friend, oh, such a Friend! He bled, He died to save me;
3. I've found a Friend, oh, such a Friend! All pow'r to Him is giv-en,
4. I've found a Friend, oh, such a Friend! So kind, and true, and ten-der,

He drew me with the cords of love, And thus He bound me to Him.
And not a-lone the gift of life, But His own self He gave me.
To guard me on my on-ward course, And bring me safe to Heav-en.
So wise a Coun-se-lor and Guide, So might-y a De-fend-er!

And 'round my heart still close-ly twine Those ties which naught can sev-er,
Naught that I have my own I call, I hold it for the Giv-er:
Th' e-ter-nal glo-ries gleam a-far, To nerve my faint en-deav-or:
From Him, who loves me now so well, What pow'r my soul can sev-er?

For I am His, and He is mine, For-ev-er and for-ev-er.
My heart, my strength, my life, my all, Are His, and His for-ev-er.
So now to watch, to work, to war, And then to rest for-ev-er.
Shall life or death, or earth or hell? No; I am His for-ev-er.

This Is My Father's World

MALTBIE D. BABCOCK

Traditional English Melody

1. This is my Fa-ther's world, And to my lis-t'ning ears All
2. This is my Fa-ther's world, And birds their car - ols raise, The
3. This is my Fa-ther's world, O let me ne'er for - get That

na - ture sings, and 'round me rings The mu - sic of the spheres.
morn-ing light the lil - y white, De - clare their Mak - er's praise.
tho' the wrong seems oft so strong, God is the Rul - er yet.

This is my Fa-ther's world, I rest me in the thought Of
This is my Fa-ther's world, He shines in all that's fair; In the
This is my Fa-ther's world, The bat - tle is not done, Je-

rocks and trees, of skies and seas—His hands the won - ders wrought.
rus - tling grass I hear Him pass, He speaks to me ev-'ry-where.
sus who died shall be sat - is - fied, And earth and heav'n be one.

116 All Beautiful the March of Days

FRANCES WHITMARSH WILE

English Folk Song
Arranged by ARTHUR S. SULLIVAN

1. All beau - ti - ful the march of days, As sea - sons come and go;
2. O'er white ex - pan - ses spark-ling pure The ra - diant morns un-fold;
3. O Thou from whose un - fath-omed law The year in beau-ty flows,

The hand that shaped the rose hath wrought The crys-tal of the snow;
The sol - emn splen-dors of the night Burn bright-er through the cold;
Thy-self the vi - sion pass - ing by In crys-tal and in rose;

Hath sent the hoar - y frost of heaven, The flow - ing wa - ters sealed,
Life mounts in ev - 'ry throb-bing vein, Love deep - ens round the hearth,
Day un - to day doth ut - ter speech, And night to night pro - claim

And laid a si - lent love - li - ness On hill and wood and field.
And clear - er sounds the an - gel-hymn, "Good will to men on earth."
In ev - er - chang - ing words of light, The won-ders of thy name.

Words used by permission

Thank You for Spring

ELEANOR HAMMOND

FAITH CHAMBERS WILSON

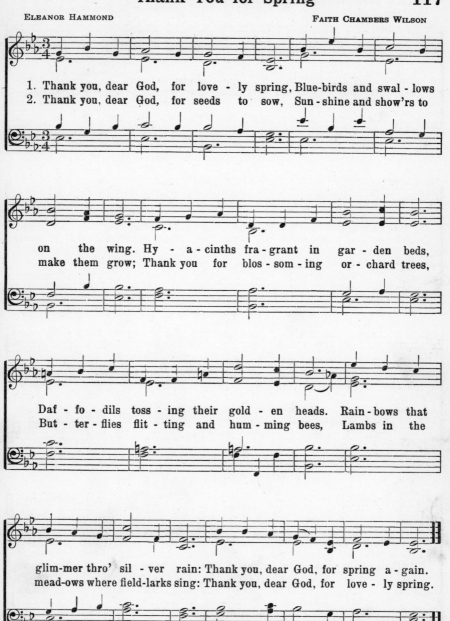

1. Thank you, dear God, for love - ly spring, Blue-birds and swal - lows
2. Thank you, dear God, for seeds to sow, Sun - shine and show'rs to

on the wing. Hy - a - cinths fra - grant in gar - den beds,
make them grow; Thank you for blos - som - ing or - chard trees,

Daf - fo - dils toss - ing their gold - en heads. Rain - bows that
But - ter - flies flit - ting and hum - ming bees, Lambs in the

glim-mer thro' sil - ver rain: Thank you, dear God, for spring a - gain.
mead-ows where field-larks sing: Thank you, dear God, for love - ly spring.

118   Praise to God for Things We See

M. M. PENSTONE   ALFRED LOWE

1. Praise to God for things we see— Grow-ing grass, the wav-ing tree,
2. Praise to God for things we hear—Voic-es of our com-rades dear,

Moth-er's face, the bright blue sky, Birds and clouds float-ing by.
Mer-ry bells and songs of birds, Sto-ries, tunes, and kind-ly words.

Praise to God for things we see, Praise to God for see-ing!
Praise to God for things we hear, Praise to God for hear-ing!

119   God, Who Made the Earth

Mrs. S. B. RHODES   R. G. McCUTCHAN

1. God, who made the earth, The air, the sky, the sea,
2. God, who made the grass, The flow'r, the fruit, the tree,
3. God, who made the sun, The moon, the stars, is He
4. God, who made all things On earth, in air, in sea,

God, Who Made the Earth

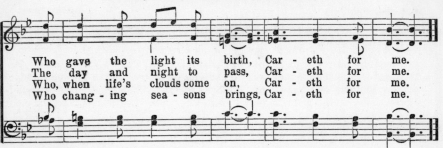

Who gave the light its birth, Car - eth for me.
The day and night to pass, Car - eth for me.
Who, when life's clouds come on, Car - eth for me.
Who chang - ing sea - sons brings, Car - eth for me.

For the Beauty of the Earth 120

Folliott S. Pierpont   Conrad Kocher

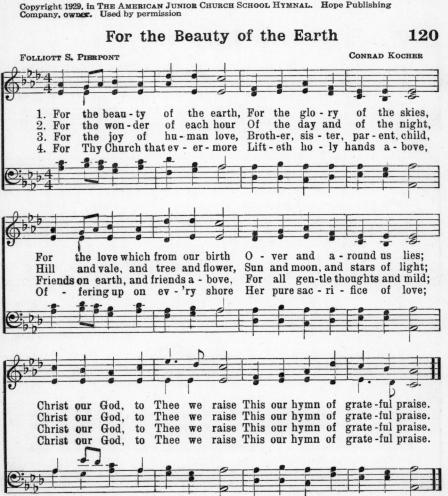

1. For the beau - ty of the earth, For the glo - ry of the skies,
2. For the won - der of each hour Of the day and of the night,
3. For the joy of hu - man love, Broth - er, sis - ter, par - ent, child,
4. For Thy Church that ev - er - more Lift - eth ho - ly hands a - bove,

For the love which from our birth O - ver and a - round us lies;
Hill and vale, and tree and flower, Sun and moon, and stars of light;
Friends on earth, and friends a - bove, For all gen - tle thoughts and mild;
Of - fering up on ev - 'ry shore Her pure sac - ri - fice of love;

Christ our God, to Thee we raise This our hymn of grate - ful praise.
Christ our God, to Thee we raise This our hymn of grate - ful praise.
Christ our God, to Thee we raise This our hymn of grate - ful praise.
Christ our God, to Thee we raise This our hymn of grate - ful praise.

121   Standing on the Promises

R. K. C.

R. KELSO CARTER

1. Stand-ing on the prom-is-es of Christ my King, Thro' e-ter-nal a-ges
2. Stand-ing on the prom-is-es that can-not fail, When the howling storms of
3. Stand-ing on the prom-is-es of Christ the Lord, Bound to Him e-ter-nal-
4. Stand-ing on the prom-is-es I can-not fall, Lis-tening ev-ery mo-ment

let His prais-es ring; Glo-ry in the high-est, I will shout and sing,
doubt and fear as-sail, By the liv-ing word of God I shall pre-vail,
ly by love's strong cord, O-ver-com-ing dai-ly with the Spir-it's sword,
to the Spir-it's call, Rest-ing in my Sav-iour, as my all in all,

CHORUS.

Stand-ing on the prom-is-es of God. Stand - ing, stand - ing,
Standing on the promises, standing on the promises,

Stand-ing on the prom-is-es of God my Sav-iour; Stand - ing,
Standing on the prom-is-es.

stand - - ing, I'm stand-ing on the prom-is-es of God.
stand-ing on the prom-is-es,

He Leadeth Me

JOSEPH H. GILMORE   WILLIAM B. BRADBURY

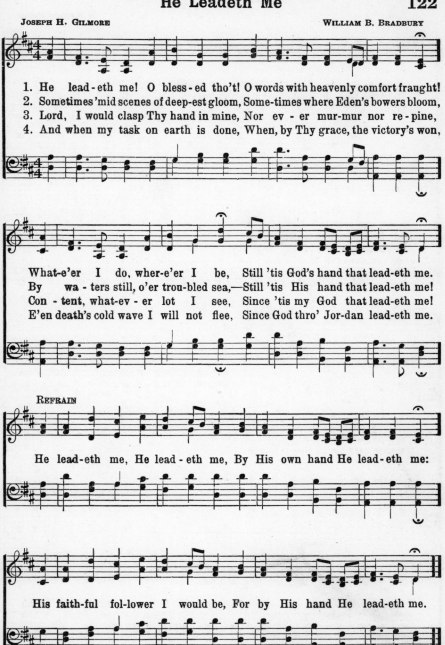

1. He lead-eth me! O bless-ed tho't! O words with heavenly comfort fraught!
2. Sometimes 'mid scenes of deep-est gloom, Some-times where Eden's bowers bloom,
3. Lord, I would clasp Thy hand in mine, Nor ev - er mur-mur nor re - pine,
4. And when my task on earth is done, When, by Thy grace, the victory's won,

What-e'er I do, wher-e'er I be, Still 'tis God's hand that lead-eth me.
By wa - ters still, o'er trou-bled sea,—Still 'tis His hand that lead-eth me!
Con - tent, what-ev - er lot I see, Since 'tis my God that lead-eth me!
E'en death's cold wave I will not flee, Since God thro' Jor-dan lead-eth me.

REFRAIN

He lead-eth me, He lead - eth me, By His own hand He lead-eth me:

His faith-ful fol-lower I would be, For by His hand He lead-eth me.

123   If Jesus Goes with Me

C. A. M.

G. Austin Miles

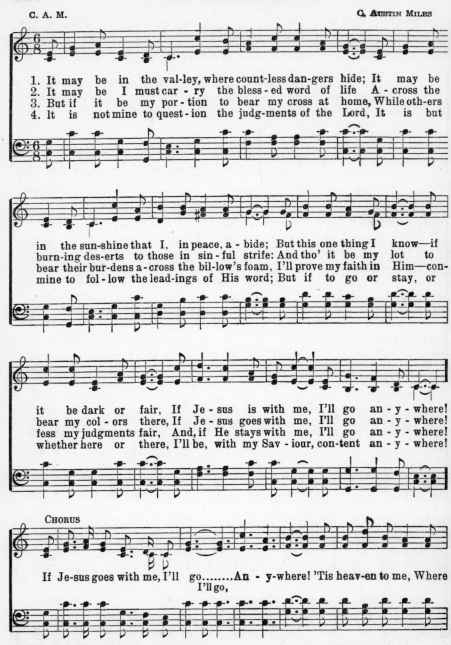

1. It may be in the val-ley, where count-less dan-gers hide; It may be
2. It may be I must car - ry the bless - ed word of life A - cross the
3. But if it be my por - tion to bear my cross at home, While oth-ers
4. It is not mine to quest - ion the judg-ments of the Lord, It is but

in the sun-shine that I, in peace, a - bide; But this one thing I know—if
burn-ing des-erts to those in sin - ful strife: And tho' it be my lot to
bear their bur-dens a-cross the bil-low's foam, I'll prove my faith in Him—con-
mine to fol-low the lead-ings of His word; But if to go or stay, or

it be dark or fair, If Je - sus is with me, I'll go an - y - where!
bear my col - ors there, If Je - sus goes with me, I'll go an - y - where!
fess my judgments fair, And, if He stays with me, I'll go an - y - where!
whether here or there, I'll be, with my Sav - iour, con-tent an - y - where!

CHORUS

If Je-sus goes with me, I'll go........An - y-where! 'Tis heav-en to me, Where
I'll go,

If Jesus Goes with Me

e'er I may be, If He is there! I count it a priv-i-lege here.... His
His cross, His

cross to bear;.. If Je-sus goes with me, I'll go An-y-where!
cross, His cross to bear;

O God, Our Help in Ages Past   124

ISAAC WATTS   WILLIAM CROFT

1. O God, our help in a-ges past, Our hope for years to come,
2. Un-der the shad-ow of Thy throne Still may we dwell se-cure;
3. Be-fore the hills in or-der stood, Or earth re-ceived her frame,
4. O God, our help in a-ges past, Our hope for years to come;

Our shel-ter from the storm-y blast, And our e-ter-nal home!
Suf-fi-cient is Thine arm a-lone, And our de-fense is sure.
From ev-er-last-ing Thou art God, To end-less years the same.
Be Thou my guide while life shall last, And our e-ter-nal home.

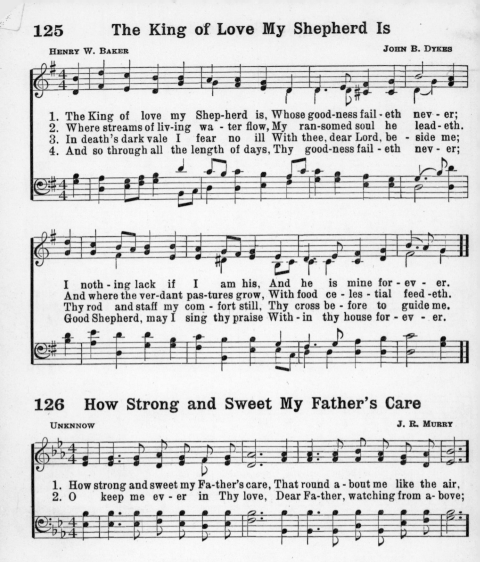

125 The King of Love My Shepherd Is

HENRY W. BAKER

JOHN B. DYKES

1. The King of love my Shep-herd is, Whose good-ness fail-eth nev-er;
2. Where streams of liv-ing wa-ter flow, My ran-somed soul he lead-eth.
3. In death's dark vale I fear no ill With thee, dear Lord, be-side me;
4. And so through all the length of days, Thy good-ness fail-eth nev-er;

I noth-ing lack if I am his, And he is mine for-ev-er.
And where the ver-dant pas-tures grow, With food ce-les-tial feed-eth.
Thy rod and staff my com-fort still, Thy cross be-fore to guide me.
Good Shepherd, may I sing thy praise With-in thy house for-ev-er.

126 How Strong and Sweet My Father's Care

UNKNNOW

J. R. MURRY

1. How strong and sweet my Fa-ther's care, That round a-bout me like the air,
2. O keep me ev-er in Thy love, Dear Fa-ther, watching from a-bove;

Is with me al-ways, ev-'ry-where; He cares for me.
And let me still Thy mer-cy prove, And care for me.

Fling Out the Banner! Let It Float 127

GEORGE W. DOANE

J. BAPTISTE CALKIN

1. Fling out the ban-ner! let it float Sky-ward and sea-ward, high and wide;
2. Fling out the ban-ner! an-gels bend In anx-ious si-lence o'er the sign,
3. Fling out the ban-ner! hea-then lands Shall see from far the glo-rious sight,
4. Fling out the ban-ner! wide and high, Sea-ward and sky-ward, let it shine:

The sun that lights its shin-ing folds The cross on which the Sav-iour died.
And vain-ly seek to com-pre-hend The wond-er of the love di-vine.
And na-tions crowd-ing to be born, Bap-tize their spir-its in its light.
Nor skill, nor might, nor mer-it ours; We con-quer on-ly in that sign.

Jesus Shall Reign 128

ISAAC WATTS

JOHN HATTON

1. Je-sus shall reign wher-e'er the sun Does his suc-ces-sive jour-neys run;
2. From north to south the princ-es meet To pay their hom-age at His feet;
3. To Him shall end-less prayer be made And end-less prais-es crown His head;
4. Peo-ple and realms of ev-'ry tongue Dwell on His love with sweet-est song,

His king-dom spread from shore to shore, Till moons shall wax and wane no more.
While west-ern em-pires own their Lord, And savage tribes at-tend His word.
His name like sweet perfume shall rise With ev-'ry morn-ing sac-ri-fice.
And in-fant voic-es shall pro-claim Their earth-ly blessings on His name.

129 Trust and Obey

J. H. SAMMIS

D. B. TOWNER

1. When we walk with the Lord In the Light of His Word What a glo-ry He
2. Not a shad-ow can rise, Not a cloud in the skies, But His smile quickly
3. Not a bur-den we bear, Not a sor-row we share, But our toil He doth
4. But we nev-er can prove The de-lights of His love Un-til all on the
5. Then in fel-low-ship sweet We will sit at His feet, Or we'll walk by His

sheds on our way! While we do His good will, He a-bides with us still,
drives it a-way; Not a doubt or a fear, Not a sigh nor a tear,
rich-ly re-pay; Not a grief nor a loss, Not a frown or a cross,
al-tar we lay; For the fa-vor He shows, And the joy He be-stows,
side in the way; What He says we will do, Where He sends we will go,—

CHORUS

And with all who will trust and o-bey.
Can a-bide while we trust and o-bey.
But is blest if we trust and o-bey.   Trust and o-bey, for there's
Are for them who will trust and o-bey.
Nev-er fear, on-ly trust and o-bey.

no oth-er way To be hap-py in Je-sus, But to trust and o-bey.

MARY THOMSON   JAMES WALSH

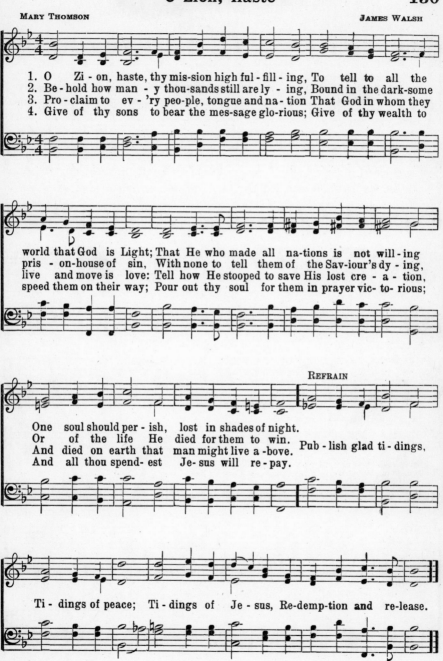

1. O Zi-on, haste, thy mis-sion high ful-fill-ing, To tell to all the
2. Be-hold how man-y thou-sands still are ly-ing, Bound in the dark-some
3. Pro-claim to ev-'ry peo-ple, tongue and na-tion That God in whom they
4. Give of thy sons to bear the mes-sage glo-rious; Give of thy wealth to

world that God is Light; That He who made all na-tions is not will-ing
pris-on-house of sin, With none to tell them of the Sav-iour's dy-ing,
live and move is love: Tell how He stooped to save His lost cre-a-tion,
speed them on their way; Pour out thy soul for them in prayer vic-to-rious;

REFRAIN

One soul should per-ish, lost in shades of night.
Or of the life He died for them to win.
And died on earth that man might live a-bove.   Pub-lish glad ti-dings,
And all thou spend-est Je-sus will re-pay.

Ti-dings of peace; Ti-dings of Je-sus, Re-demp-tion and re-lease.

131 Pledge to All Lands

NANCY BYRD TURNER

S. K. EMURIAN

Not too fast

Shall we not send to oth-er lands The bless-ed Bi-ble sto-ry?

Shall we not share with chil-dren there His won-drous pow'r and glo-ry?

We will not rest 'til they have heard The won-ders of God's ho-ly Word.

We will not rest 'til they have heard The won-ders of God's ho-ly Word.

132 Blest Be the Tie

JOHN FAWCETT

HANS G. NÄGELI

1. Blest be the tie that binds Our hearts in Chris-tian love;
2. Be - fore our Fa-ther's throne, We pour our ar - dent prayers;
3. We share our mu - tual woes, Our mu - tual bur - dens bear;
4. When we a - sun - der part, It gives us in - ward pain;

Blest Be the Tie

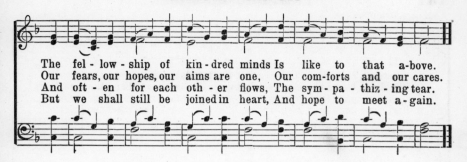

The fel-low-ship of kin-dred minds Is like to that a-bove.
Our fears, our hopes, our aims are one, Our com-forts and our cares.
And oft-en for each oth-er flows, The sym-pa-thiz-ing tear.
But we shall still be joined in heart, And hope to meet a-gain.

Sweeter than the Day Before   133

ROBERT C. LOVELESS   WENDELL P. LOVELESS

Ev-'ry day with Je-sus Is sweet-er than the day be-fore;

Ev-'ry day with Je-sus, I love Him more and more;

Je-sus saves and keeps me, And He's the One I'm liv-ing for;

Ev-'ry day with Je-sus Is sweet-er than the day be-fore.

134 **Send the Light**

C. H. G.

CHARLES H. GABRIEL

1. There's a call comes ring-ing o'er the rest-less wave, "Send the light! . . .
2. We have heard the Mac - e - do-nian call to - day, "Send the light! . . .
3. Let us pray that grace may ev-ery-where a-bound; Send the light! . . .
4. Let us not grow wea-ry in the work of love, Send the light! . . .

Send the light!

Send the light!" There are souls to res-cue, there are souls to save,
Send the light!" And a gold - en of-fering at the cross we lay,
Send the light! And a Christ-like spir - it ev-ery-where be found,
Send the light! Let us gath-er jew-els for a crown a - bove,

Send the light!

REFRAIN

Send the light! . . . Send the light! . . . Send the light! . . . the

Send the light! Send the light! Send the light!

1

bless - ed gos - pel light; Let it shine . . . . from shore to

the bless - ed gos - pel light; Let it shine

2

shore! . . . . shine . . . for - ev - er - more. . . . .

from shore to shore! Let it shine for - ev - er - more.

E. E. HEWITT

JOHN R. SWENEY

1. There's sun-shine in my soul to-day, More glo-ri-ous and bright
2. There's mu-sic in my soul to-day, A car-ol to my King,
3. There's springtime in my soul to-day, For, when the Lord is near,
4. There's glad-ness in my soul to-day, And hope and praise and love,

Than glows in an-y earth-ly sky, For Je-sus is my light.
And Je-sus, lis-ten-ing, can hear The songs I can-not sing.
The dove of peace sings in my heart, The flow'rs of grace ap-pear.
For bless-ings which He gives me now, For joys "laid up" a-bove.

REFRAIN

O there's sun - - shine, bless-ed sun - - shine,
O there's sun-shine in my soul, bless-ed sun-shine in my soul,

While the peace-ful, hap-py mo-ments roll; When
hap-py mo-ments roll;

Je-sus shows His smil-ing face, There is sun-shine in my soul.

I Love to Tell the Story

CATHERINE HANKEY   WILLIAM G. FISCHER

1. I love to tell the sto - ry Of un - seen things a - bove, Of Je - sus and His glo - ry, Of Je - sus and His love. I love to tell the sto - ry, Be - cause I know 'tis true; It sat - is - fies my long-ings As noth-ing else can do.

2. I love to tell the sto - ry, More won - der - ful it seems Than all the gold - en fan - cies Of all our gold - en dreams. I love to tell the sto - ry, It did so much for me; And that is just the rea - son I tell it now to thee.

3. I love to tell the sto - ry, 'Tis pleas - ant to re - peat What seems, each time I tell it, More won - der - ful - ly sweet. I love to tell the sto - ry, For some have nev - er heard The mes-sage of sal - va - tion From God's own ho - ly Word.

4. I love to tell the sto - ry, For those who know it best Seem hun - ger - ing and thirst-ing To hear it like the rest. And when, in scenes of glo - ry, I sing the new, new song, 'Twill be the old, old sto - ry That I have loved so long.

CHORUS

I love to tell the sto - ry, 'Twill be my theme in glo - ry To tell the old, old sto - ry Of Je-sus and His love.

We've a Story to Tell

Colin Sterne

H. E. Nichol

1. We've a sto - ry to tell to the na - tions, That shall
2. We've a song to be sung to the na - tions, That shall
3. We've a mes - sage to give to the na - tions, That the
4. We've a Sav - iour to show to the na - tions, Who the

turn their hearts to the right; A sto - ry of truth and sweet-ness,
lift their hearts to the Lord; A song that shall con - quer e - vil
Lord who reign-eth a - bove, Hath sent us His Son to save us,
path of sor - row has trod, That all of the world's great peo - ple

A sto - ry of peace and light, A sto - ry of peace and light.
And shat-ter the spear and sword, And shat-ter the spear and sword.
And show us that God is love, And show us that God is love.
Might come to the truth of God, Might come to the truth of God!

REFRAIN

For the darkness shall turn to dawn - ing, And the dawn-ing to noon-day bright,

And Christ's great kingdom shall come on earth, The king-dom of love and light.

138 The Whole Wide World for Jesus

J. Dempster Hammond

John H. Maunder

1. The whole wide world for Je-sus! This shall our watch-word be;
2. The whole wide world for Je-sus! In-spires us with the thought
3. The whole wide world for Je-sus! The march-ing or-der sound:

Up-on the high-est moun-tain, Down by the wid-est sea;
That all God's wan-d'ring chil-dren Have by His love been sought.
Go ye and preach the Gos-pel Wher-ev-er man is found.

The whole wide world for Je-sus! To Him shall all men bow,
The whole wide world for Je-sus! O faint not by the way!
The whole wide world for Je-sus! Ride forth, O conqu'ring King,

In cit-y or in prai-rie—The world for Je-sus now!
The cross shall sure-ly con-quer In this our glo-rious day.
Thro' all the might-y na-tions The world to glo-ry bring!

REFRAIN

The whole wide world, The whole wide world—Pro-claim the Gospel tid-ings thro'

The Whole Wide World for Jesus

The whole wide world; Lift up the cross for Je-sus, His ban-ner be un-furled,

Till ev-'ry tongue con-fess Him thro' The whole wide world!

Somebody

139

JOHN R. CLEMENTS

W. S. WEEDEN

1. Some-bod-y did a gold-en deed, Prov-ing him-self a friend in need;
2. Some-bod-y tho't 'tis sweet to live, Will-ing-ly said, "I'm glad to give;"
3. Some-bod-y made a lov-ing gift, Cheer-ful-ly tried a load to lift;
4. Some-bod-y i - dled all the hours, Care-less-ly crushed life's fair-est flow'rs;
5. Some-bod-y filled the days with light, Con-stant-ly chased a - way the night;

Some-bod-y sang a cheer-ful song, Bright'ning the sky the whole day long—
Some-bod-y fought a val - iant fight, Brave-ly he lived to shield the right—
Some-bod-y told the love of Christ, Told how His will was sac - ri - ficed—
Some-bod-y made life loss, not gain, Tho't-less-ly seemed to live in vain—
Some-bod-y's work bore joy and peace, Sure - ly his life will nev-er cease—

rit.

Was that some-bod - y you?... Was that some-bod - y you?

From Greenland's Icy Mountains

REGINALD HEBER   LOWELL MASON

1. From Green-land's i - cy moun-tains, From In - dia's cor - al strand;
2. What though the spi - cy breez - es Blow soft o'er Cey-lon's isle;
3. Shall we, whose souls are light - ed With wis-dom from on high,
4. Waft, waft, ye winds, His sto - ry, And you, ye wa - ters, roll,

Where Af - ric's sun - ny foun-tains Roll down their gold - en sand:
Though ev - ery pros - pect pleas - es, And on - ly man is vile?
Shall we to men be - night - ed The lamp of life de - ny?
Till, like a sea of glo - ry, It spreads from pole to pole:

From man-y an an - cient riv - er, From man-y a palm-y plain,
In vain with lav - ish kind - ness The gifts of God are strown;
Sal - va - tion! O sal - va - tion! The joy - ful sound pro - claim,
Till o'er our ran-somed na - ture The Lamb for sin - ners slain,

They call us to de - liv - er Their land from er - ror's chain.
The hea - then in his blind - ness Bows down to wood and stone.
Till earth's re - mot - est na - tion Has learned Mes - si - ah's name.
Re - deem - er, King, Cre - a - tor, In bliss re - turns to reign.

I Will Sing the Wondrous Story 141

F. H. ROWLEY

PETER P. BILHORN

1. I will sing the won-drous sto - ry   Of the Christ who died for me,
2. I was lost, but Je - sus found me, Found the sheep that went a - stray,
3. I was bruised, but Je - sus healed me; Faint was I   from man-y a fall;
4. Days of dark-ness still come o'er me, Sor-row's paths I   of - ten tread,
5. He will keep me till the riv - er   Rolls its wa - ters at my feet;

How He left His home in glo - ry   For the cross of Cal - va - ry.
Threw His lov - ing arms a - round me, Drew me back in - to His way.
Sight was gone, and fears pos-sessed me, But He freed me from them all.
But the Sav - iour still is with me; By His hand I'm safe - ly led.
Then He'll bear me safe - ly o - ver, Where the loved ones I shall meet.

CHORUS

Yes, I'll sing .... the won-drous sto - ry   Of the
Yes, I'll sing   the won-drous sto - ry

Christ ... who died for me, ... Sing it with .... the saints in
Of the Christ   who died for me,   Sing it with

glo - - ry, Gath-ered by .... the crys-tal sea.
the saints in glo - ry,   Gath-ered by   the crys-tal sea.

142

Bring Them In

ALEXCENAH THOMAS

W. A. OGDEN

1. Hark! 'tis the Shep-herd's voice I hear, Out in the des - ert dark and drear,
2. Who'll go and help this Shep-herd kind, Help Him the wan-d'ring ones to find?
3. Out in the des-ert hear their cry, Out on the mountain wild and high;

Call-ing the sheep who've gone a-stray, Far from the Shep-herd's fold a-way.
Who'll bring the lost ones to the fold, Where they'll be sheltered from the cold?
Hark!' 'tis the Mas-ter speaks to thee, "Go find My sheep wher-e'er they be."

CHORUS

Bring them in, bring them in, Bring them in from the fields of sin;

Bring them in, bring them in, Bring the wan-d'ring ones to Je - sus.

143

In Christ There Is No East or West

JOHN OXENHAM

ALEXANDER R. REINAGLE

1. In Christ there is no East or West, In Him no South or North;
2. In Him shall true hearts ev - 'ry-where Their high com - mun - ion find;
3. Join hands then, broth-ers of the faith, What-e'er your race may be;
4. In Christ now meet both East and West, In Him meet South and North;

In Christ There Is No East or West

But one great fel - low - ship of love Thro' - out the whole wide earth.
His serv - ice is the gold - en cord Close - bind - ing all man - kind.
Who serves my Fa - ther as a son Is sure - ly kin to me.
All Christ - ly souls are one in Him Thro' - out the whole wide earth.

Let the Song Go Round the Earth   144

S. G. S.   SARAH G. STOCK

1. Let the song go round the earth, Je - sus Christ is Lord!
2. Let the song go round the earth, From the east - ern sea,
3. Let the song go round the earth, Where the sum - mer smiles;
4. Let the song go round the earth, Je - sus Christ is King!

Sound His prais - es, tell His worth, Be His name a - dored;
Where the day - light has its birth, Glad and bright and free;
Let the notes of ho - ly mirth Break from dis - tant isles;
With the sto - ry of His worth Let the whole earth ring;

Ev - 'ry clime and ev - 'ry tongue Join the grand, the glo - rious song!
Chi - na's mil - lions join the strains, Waft them on to In - dia's plains.
In - land for - ests, dark and dim, Ice-bound coasts give back the hymn.
Him cre - a - tion all a - dore Ev - er - more and ev - er - more.

O Word of God Incarnate

WILLIAM WALSHAM HOW   "Meiningen Gesangbuch"

1. O Word of God in-car-nate, O Wis-dom from on high,
2. The Church from her dear Mas-ter Re-ceived the gift di-vine,
3. It float-eth like a ban-ner Be-fore God's host un-furled;
4. O make Thy Church, dear Sav-iour, A lamp of pur-est gold,

O Truth un-changed, un-chang-ing, O Light of our dark sky:
And still that light she lift-eth O'er all the earth to shine.
It shin-eth like a bea-con A-bove the dark-ling world;
To bear be-fore the na-tions Thy true light, as of old.

We praise Thee for the ra-diance That from the hal-lowed page,
It is the gold-en cas-ket, Where gems of truth are stored;
It is the chart and com-pass That o'er life's surg-ing sea,
O teach Thy wan-dering pil-grims By this their path to trace,

A lan-tern to our foot-steps, Shines on from age to age.
It is the heaven-drawn pic-ture Of Christ, the liv-ing Word.
'Mid mists and rocks and dark-ness, Still guides, O Christ, to Thee.
Till, clouds and dark-ness end-ed, They see Thee face to face.

Thy Word Have I Hid in My Heart   146

Adapted by E. O. S.

E. O. SELLERS

1. Thy Word is a lamp to my feet, A light to my path al-way;
2. For-ev-er, O Lord, is Thy Word Es-tab-lished and fixed on high;
3. At morn-ing, at noon, and at night I ev-er will give Thee praise;
4. Thro' Him whom Thy Word hath foretold, The Sav-iour and Morn-ing Star,

To guide and to save me from sin, And show me the heaven-ly way.
Thy faith-ful-ness un-to all men A-bid-eth for-ev-er nigh.
For Thou art my por-tion, O Lord, And shall be through all my days!
Sal-va-tion and peace have been bro't To those who have strayed a-far.

CHORUS—PSALM 119: 11

Thy Word have I hid in my heart, ... That I might not
in my heart,

sin a-gainst Thee, ... That I might not sin, That
a-gainst Thee,

I might not sin, Thy Word have I hid in my heart.

147 — Book of Books

PERCY DEARMER

JOHANN R. AHLE

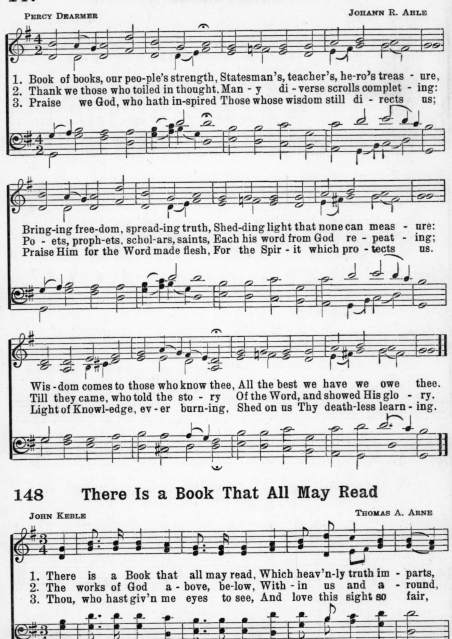

1. Book of books, our peo-ple's strength, Statesman's, teacher's, he-ro's treas - ure,
2. Thank we those who toiled in thought, Man - y di - verse scrolls complet - ing:
3. Praise we God, who hath in-spired Those whose wisdom still di - rects us;

Bring-ing free-dom, spread-ing truth, Shed-ding light that none can meas - ure:
Po - ets, proph-ets, schol-ars, saints, Each his word from God re - peat - ing;
Praise Him for the Word made flesh, For the Spir - it which pro - tects us.

Wis - dom comes to those who know thee, All the best we have we owe thee.
Till they came, who told the sto - ry Of the Word, and showed His glo - ry.
Light of Knowl-edge, ev - er burn-ing, Shed on us Thy death-less learn - ing.

148 — There Is a Book That All May Read

JOHN KEBLE

THOMAS A. ARNE

1. There is a Book that all may read, Which heav'n-ly truth im - parts,
2. The works of God a - bove, be-low, With - in us and a - round,
3. Thou, who hast giv'n me eyes to see, And love this sight so fair,

There Is a Book That All May Read

And all the lore its schol-ars need, Pure eyes and Chris-tian hearts.
Are pa-ges in that Book, to show How God Him-self is found.
Give me a heart to find out Thee, And read Thee ev - 'ry - where.

Wonderful Words of Life   149

P. P. B.   P. P. Bliss

1. Sing them o - ver a - gain to me, Won - der - ful words of Life;
2. Christ, the bless-ed One, gives to all, Won - der - ful words of Life;
3. Sweet-ly ech - o the gos - pel call, Won - der - ful words of Life;

Let me more of their beau - ty see, Won - der - ful words of Life.
Sin - ner, list to the lov - ing call, Won - der - ful words of Life.
Of - fer par - don and peace to all, Won - der - ful words of Life.

Words of life and beau - ty, Teach me faith and du - ty:
All so free - ly giv - en, Woo - ing us to heav - en:
Je - sus, on - ly Sav - iour, Sanc - ti - fy for - ev - er:

REFRAIN

Beau-ti-ful words, won-der-ful words, Won-der-ful words of Life.   Life.

150 Thy Word Is Like a Garden, Lord

T. H. GILL

Old Melody

1. Thy Word is like a gar-den, Lord, With flow-ers bright and fair;
2. Thy Word is like a star-ry host: A thou-sand rays of light
3. O may I love Thy pre-cious Word, May I ex-plore the mine,

And ev-'ry one who seeks may pluck A love-ly clust-er there.
Are seen to guide the trav-el-er, And make his path-way bright.
May I its fra-grant flow-ers glean, May light up-on me shine!

Thy Word is like a deep, deep mine; And jew-els rich and rare
Thy Word is like an ar-mo-ry, Where sol-diers may re-pair;
O may I find my ar-mor there! Thy Word my trust-y sword,

Are hid-den in its might-y depths For ev-'ry search-er there.
And find, for life's long bat-tle-day, All need-ful weap-ons there.
I'll learn to fight with ev-'ry foe The bat-tle of the Lord.

151 Holy Bible, Book Divine

JOHN BURTON

WILLIAM B. BRADBURY

1. Ho-ly Bi-ble, Book di-vine, Pre-cious treas-ure, thou art mine;
2. Mine to chide me when I rove; Mine to show a Sav-iour's love;
3. Mine to com-fort in dis-tress, Suf-fering in this wil-der-ness;
4. Mine to tell of joys to come, And the reb-el sin-ner's doom;

Holy Bible, Book Divine

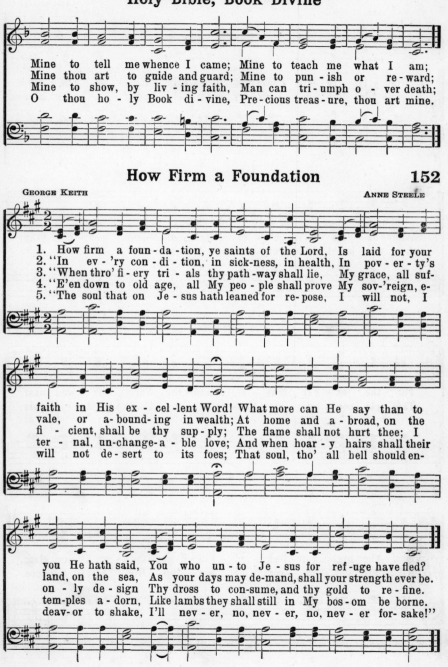

Mine to tell me whence I came; Mine to teach me what I am;
Mine thou art to guide and guard; Mine to pun-ish or re-ward;
Mine to show, by liv-ing faith, Man can tri-umph o-ver death;
O thou ho-ly Book di-vine, Pre-cious treas-ure, thou art mine.

How Firm a Foundation   152

GEORGE KEITH   ANNE STEELE

1. How firm a foun-da-tion, ye saints of the Lord, Is laid for your
2. "In ev-'ry con-di-tion, in sick-ness, in health, In pov-er-ty's
3. "When thro' fi-er-y tri-als thy path-way shall lie, My grace, all suf-
4. "E'en down to old age, all My peo-ple shall prove My sov-'reign, e-
5. "The soul that on Je-sus hath leaned for re-pose, I will not, I

faith in His ex-cel-lent Word! What more can He say than to
vale, or a-bound-ing in wealth; At home and a-broad, on the
fi-cient, shall be thy sup-ply; The flame shall not hurt thee; I
ter-nal, un-change-a-ble love; And when hoar-y hairs shall their
will not de-sert to its foes; That soul, tho' all hell should en-

you He hath said, You who un-to Je-sus for ref-uge have fled?
land, on the sea, As your days may de-mand, shall your strength ever be.
on-ly de-sign Thy dross to con-sume, and thy gold to re-fine.
tem-ples a-dorn, Like lambs they shall still in My bos-om be borne.
deav-or to shake, I'll nev-er, no, nev-er, no, nev-er for-sake!"

153 Houses of Worship

EDITH LOVELL THOMAS

CHARLES F. GOUNOD
Arranged by J. W. COLE

1. Glad-ly to the house of wor-ship Come we to-day,
2. Some de-light in coun-try chap-el Built on a hill;

Thanks to give for qui-et church-es Where peo-ple pray;
Oth-ers kneel in great ca-the-dral Dim lit and still;

For the or-gan mus-ic sound-ing Far off and near;
Tem-ple con-gre-ga-tions sing the Psalms loved of yore;

For the high sun-light-ed win-dows, Col-ored or clear.
All are set a-part for wor-ship, God to a-dore.

The Church's One Foundation

154

SAMUEL J. STONE

SAMUEL S. WESLEY

1. The Church-'s one foun-da-tion Is Je-sus Christ her Lord;
2. E-lect from ev-ery na-tion, Yet one o'er all the earth,
3. 'Mid toil and trib-u-la-tion, And tu-mult of her war,
4. Yet she on earth hath un-ion With God the Three in One,

She is His new cre-a-tion By Spir-it and the Word:
Her char-ter of sal-va-tion, One Lord, one faith, one birth;
She waits the con-sum-ma-tion Of peace for-ev-er-more;
And mys-tic sweet com-mun-ion With those whose rest is won:

From heaven He came and sought her To be His ho-ly bride;
One ho-ly name she bless-es, Par-takes one ho-ly food,
Till, with the vi-sion glo-rious, Her long-ing eyes are blest,
O hap-py ones and ho-ly! Lord, give us grace that we,

With His own blood He bought her, And for her life He died.
And to one hope she press-es, With ev-ery grace en-dued.
And the great Church vic-to-rious Shall be the Church at rest.
Like them, the meek and low-ly, On high may dwell with Thee.

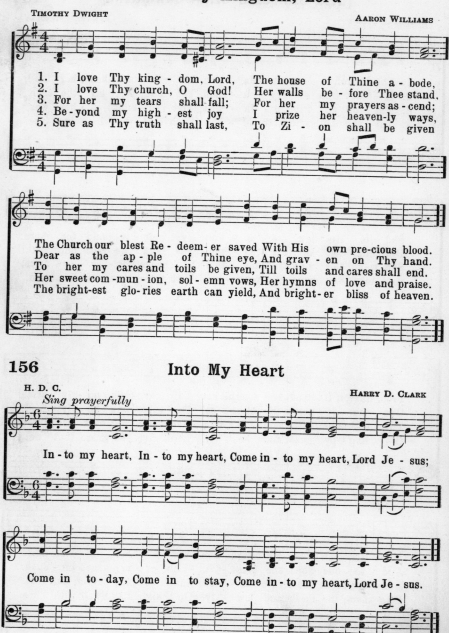

155   I Love Thy Kingdom, Lord

TIMOTHY DWIGHT

AARON WILLIAMS

1. I love Thy king - dom, Lord, The house of Thine a - bode,
2. I love Thy church, O God! Her walls be - fore Thee stand.
3. For her my tears shall fall; For her my prayers as - cend;
4. Be - yond my high - est joy I prize her heaven-ly ways,
5. Sure as Thy truth shall last, To Zi - on shall be given

The Church our blest Re - deem - er saved With His own pre-cious blood.
Dear as the ap - ple of Thine eye, And grav - en on Thy hand.
To her my cares and toils be given, Till toils and cares shall end.
Her sweet com - mun - ion, sol - emn vows, Her hymns of love and praise.
The bright-est glo - ries earth can yield, And bright - er bliss of heaven.

156   Into My Heart

H. D. C.

Sing prayerfully

HARRY D. CLARK

In - to my heart, In - to my heart, Come in - to my heart, Lord Je - sus;

Come in to - day, Come in to stay, Come in - to my heart, Lord Je - sus.

Open My Eyes, That I May See 157

C. H. S.

CHARLES H. SCOTT

1. O - pen my eyes, that I may see Glimps-es of truth Thou hast for me;
2. O - pen my ears, that I may hear Voic - es of truth Thou send-est clear;
3. O - pen my mouth, and let me bear Glad - ly the warm truth ev-ery-where;

Place in my hands the won-der-ful key That shall un-clasp, and set me free.
And while the wave-notes fall on my ear, Ev - ery-thing false will dis - ap-pear.
O - pen my heart, and let me pre-pare Love with Thy chil-dren thus to share.

Si - lent-ly now I wait for Thee, Read-y, my God, Thy will to see;
Si - lent-ly now I wait for Thee, Read-y, my God, Thy will to see;
Si - lent-ly now I wait for Thee, Read-y, my God, Thy will to see;

O - pen my eyes, il - lu - mine me, Spir - it di - vine!
O - pen my ears, il - lu - mine me, Spir - it di - vine!
O - pen my heart, il - lu - mine me, Spir - it di - vine!

158   I Know Whom I Have Believed

Daniel W. Whittle   James McGranahan

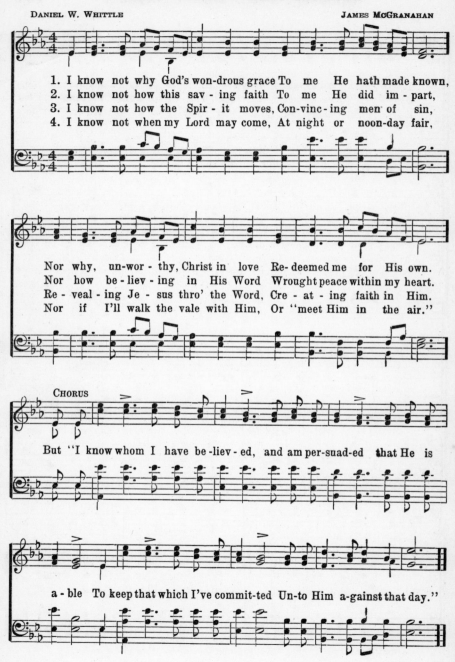

1. I know not why God's won-drous grace To me He hath made known,
2. I know not how this sav - ing faith To me He did im - part,
3. I know not how the Spir - it moves, Con-vinc-ing men of sin,
4. I know not when my Lord may come, At night or noon-day fair,

Nor why, un-wor - thy, Christ in love Re-deemed me for His own.
Nor how be - liev - ing in His Word Wrought peace within my heart.
Re - veal - ing Je - sus thro' the Word, Cre - at - ing faith in Him.
Nor if I'll walk the vale with Him, Or "meet Him in the air."

CHORUS

But "I know whom I have be -liev - ed, and am per-suad-ed that He is

a - ble To keep that which I've commit-ted Un-to Him a-gainst that day."

C. A. M.

C. Austin Miles

1. I come to the gar-den a-lone, While the dew is still on the
2. He speaks, and the sound of His voice Is so sweet the birds hush their
3. I'd stay in the gar-den with Him Though the night a-round me be

ros - es, And the voice I hear, Fall-ing on my ear, The
sing - ing, And the mel - o - dy That He gave to me, With-
fall - ing, But He bids me go; Thro' the voice of woe His

CHORUS

Son of God dis-clos - es.
in my heart is ring - ing. And He walks with me, and He
voice to me is call - ing.

talks with me, And He tells me I am His own; And the

joy we share as we tar - ry there, None oth-er has ev - er known.

Sweet Hour of Prayer

W. W. WALFORD

WILLIAM B. BRADBURY

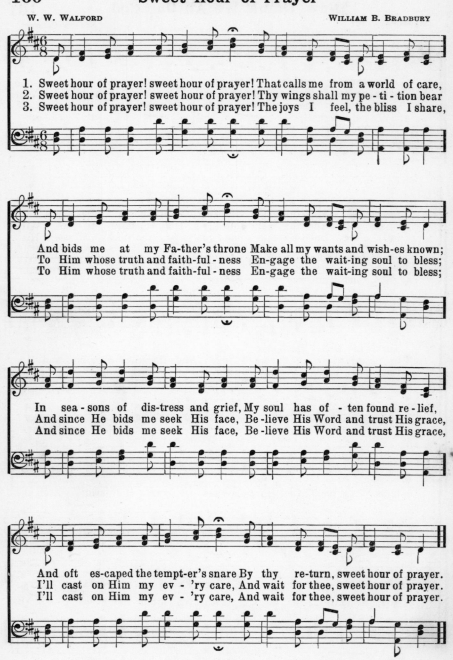

1. Sweet hour of prayer! sweet hour of prayer! That calls me from a world of care,
2. Sweet hour of prayer! sweet hour of prayer! Thy wings shall my pe - ti - tion bear
3. Sweet hour of prayer! sweet hour of prayer! The joys I feel, the bliss I share,

And bids me at my Fa-ther's throne Make all my wants and wish-es known;
To Him whose truth and faith-ful - ness En-gage the wait-ing soul to bless;
To Him whose truth and faith-ful - ness En-gage the wait-ing soul to bless;

In sea-sons of dis-tress and grief, My soul has of - ten found re-lief,
And since He bids me seek His face, Be-lieve His Word and trust His grace,
And since He bids me seek His face, Be-lieve His Word and trust His grace,

And oft es-caped the tempt-er's snare By thy re-turn, sweet hour of prayer.
I'll cast on Him my ev - 'ry care, And wait for thee, sweet hour of prayer.
I'll cast on Him my ev - 'ry care, And wait for thee, sweet hour of prayer.

Now Thank We All Our God

MARTIN RINKART
Translated by CATHERINE WINKWORTH

JOHANN CRÜGER

1. Now thank we all our God With heart and hands and voic - es,
2. O may this boun - teous God Thro' all our life be near us,
3. All praise and thanks to God, The Fa - ther, now be giv - en,

Who won-drous things hath done, In whom His world re - joic - es;
With ev - er - joy - ful hearts And bless - ed peace to cheer us;
The Son, and Him who reigns With them in high - est heav - en,

Who, from our moth - ers' arms, Hath blessed us on our way
And keep us in His grace, And guide us when per - plexed,
The one e - ter - nal God, Whom earth and heaven a - dore;

With count - less gifts of love, And still is ours to - day.
And free us from all ills In this world and the next.
For thus it was, is now, And shall be ev - er - more.

The Star-Spangled Banner

FRANCIS SCOTT KEY

JOHN S. SMITH

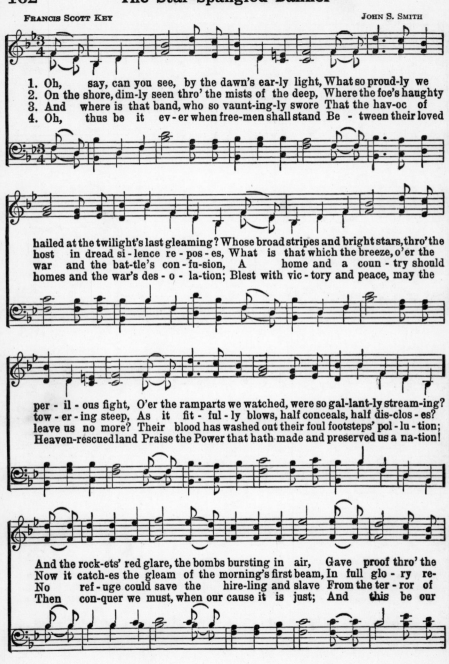

1. Oh,   say, can you see, by the dawn's ear-ly light, What so proud-ly we
2. On the shore, dim-ly seen thro' the mists of the deep, Where the foe's haughty
3. And   where is that band, who so vaunt-ing-ly swore That the hav-oc of
4. Oh,   thus be it   ev - er when free-men shall stand Be - tween their loved

hailed at the twilight's last gleaming? Whose broad stripes and bright stars, thro' the
host   in dread si - lence re - pos - es, What is that which the breeze, o'er the
war and the bat-tle's con - fu-sion, A   home and a coun - try should
homes and the war's des - o - la-tion; Blest with vic - tory and peace, may the

per - il - ous fight, O'er the ramparts we watched, were so gal-lant-ly stream-ing?
tow - er - ing steep, As it fit - ful - ly blows, half conceals, half dis-clos - es?
leave us no more? Their blood has washed out their foul footsteps' pol - lu - tion;
Heaven-rescued land Praise the Power that hath made and preserved us a na-tion!

And the rock-ets' red glare, the bombs bursting in air,   Gave proof thro' the
Now it catch-es the gleam of the morning's first beam, In full glo - ry re-
No   ref - uge could save the   hire-ling and slave From the ter - ror of
Then   con-quer we must, when our cause it is just; And   this be our

The Star-Spangled Banner

CHORUS.

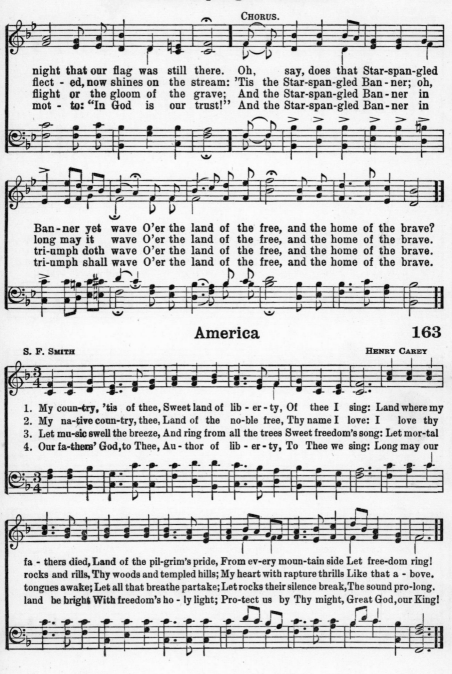

night that our flag was still there. Oh, say, does that Star-span-gled
flect - ed, now shines on the stream: 'Tis the Star-span-gled Ban - ner; oh,
flight or the gloom of the grave; And the Star-span-gled Ban - ner in
mot - to: "In God is our trust!" And the Star-span-gled Ban - ner in

Ban-ner yet wave O'er the land of the free, and the home of the brave?
long may it wave O'er the land of the free, and the home of the brave.
tri-umph doth wave O'er the land of the free, and the home of the brave.
tri-umph shall wave O'er the land of the free, and the home of the brave.

America
163

S. F. SMITH
HENRY CAREY

1. My coun-try, 'tis of thee, Sweet land of lib - er - ty, Of thee I sing: Land where my
2. My na-tive coun-try, thee, Land of the no-ble free, Thy name I love: I love thy
3. Let mu-sic swell the breeze, And ring from all the trees Sweet freedom's song: Let mor-tal
4. Our fa-thers' God, to Thee, Au - thor of lib - er - ty, To Thee we sing: Long may our

fa - thers died, Land of the pil-grim's pride, From ev-ery moun-tain side Let free-dom ring!
rocks and rills, Thy woods and templed hills; My heart with rapture thrills Like that a - bove.
tongues awake; Let all that breathe partake; Let rocks their silence break, The sound pro-long.
land be bright With freedom's ho - ly light; Pro-tect us by Thy might, Great God, our King!

164 America the Beautiful

KATHARINE LEE BATES

SAMUEL A. WARD

1. O beau - ti - ful for spa-cious skies, For am - ber waves of grain,
2. O beau - ti - ful for pil - grim feet, Whose stern, im-pas-sioned stress
3. O beau - ti - ful for he - roes proved In lib - er - at - ing strife,
4. O beau - ti - ful for pa - triot dream That sees be - yond the years

For pur - ple moun-tain maj - es - ties A - bove the fruit-ed plain!
A thor - ough-fare for free - dom beat A - cross the wil - der - ness!
Who more than self their coun - try loved, And mer - cy more than life!
Thine al - a - bas - ter cit - ies gleam, Un-dimmed by hu - man tears!

A - mer - i - ca! A - mer - i - ca! God shed His grace on thee
A - mer - i - ca! A - mer - i - ca! God mend thine ev - ery flaw,
A - mer - i - ca! A - mer - i - ca! May God thy gold re - fine,
A - mer - i - ca! A - mer - i - ca! God shed His grace on thee,

And crown thy good with broth - er-hood From sea to shin - ing sea.
Con - firm thy soul in self - con-trol, Thy lib - er - ty in law.
Till all suc - cess be no - ble-ness, And ev - ery gain di - vine.
And crown thy good with broth - er-hood From sea to shin - ing sea.

Come, Ye Thankful People

165

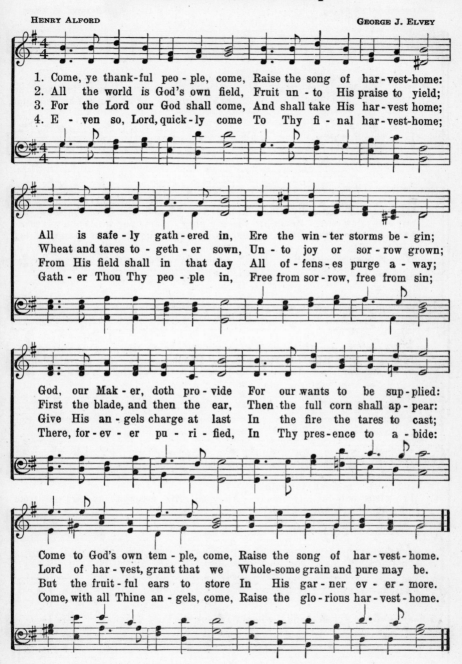

HENRY ALFORD

GEORGE J. ELVEY

1. Come, ye thank-ful peo - ple, come, Raise the song of har-vest-home:
2. All the world is God's own field, Fruit un - to His praise to yield;
3. For the Lord our God shall come, And shall take His har-vest home;
4. E - ven so, Lord, quick-ly come To Thy fi - nal har-vest-home;

All is safe - ly gath-ered in, Ere the win - ter storms be - gin;
Wheat and tares to - geth - er sown, Un - to joy or sor - row grown;
From His field shall in that day All of - fens - es purge a - way;
Gath - er Thou Thy peo - ple in, Free from sor - row, free from sin;

God, our Mak - er, doth pro - vide For our wants to be sup - plied:
First the blade, and then the ear, Then the full corn shall ap - pear:
Give His an - gels charge at last In the fire the tares to cast;
There, for - ev - er pu - ri - fied, In Thy pres - ence to a - bide:

Come to God's own tem - ple, come, Raise the song of har - vest - home.
Lord of har - vest, grant that we Whole-some grain and pure may be.
But the fruit - ful ears to store In His gar - ner ev - er - more.
Come, with all Thine an - gels, come, Raise the glo - rious har - vest - home.

166   We Plough the Fields

Matthias Claudius
Translated by Jane M. Campbell

Johann A. P. Schulz

1. We plough the fields, and scat-ter The good seed on the land, But it is
2. He on-ly is the Mak-er Of all things near and far; He paints the
3. We thank Thee, then, O Fa-ther, For all things bright and good; The seed-time

fed and wa-tered By God's al-might-y hand; He sends the snow in
way-side flow-er, He lights the eve-ning star; The winds and waves o-
and the har-vest, Our life, our health, our food; No gifts have we to

win-ter, The warmth to swell the grain, The breez-es and the sun-shine,
bey Him, By Him the birds are fed; Much more to us, His chil-dren,
of-fer For all Thy love im-parts, But that which Thou de-sir-est,

REFRAIN

And soft re-fresh-ing rain.
He gives our dai-ly bread.   All good gifts a-round us Are sent from
Our hum-ble, thank-ful hearts.

heav'n a-bove; Then thank the Lord, O thank the Lord For all His love.

Faith of Our Mothers

167

A. B. PATTEN

H. F. HEMY
Arranged by JAMES G. WALTON

1. Faith of our moth-ers, liv-ing still In cra-dle song and bed-time prayer:
2. Faith of our moth-ers, lov-ing faith, Fount of our childhood's trust and grace,
3. Faith of our moth-ers, guiding faith, For youthful long-ing, youth-ful doubt,
4. Faith of our moth-ers, Christian faith, In truth be-yond our stumbling creeds,

In nurs-ery lore and fire-side love, Thy pres-ence still per-vades the air.
Oh, may thy con - se - cra-tion prove Source of a fin - er, no - bler race;
How blurred our vi-sion, blind our way, Thy prov - i - den-tial care with-out.
Still serve the home and save the Church, And breathe thy spir-it thro' our deeds;

Faith of our moth-ers, liv - ing faith, We will be true to thee till death.
Faith of our moth-ers, lov - ing faith, We will be true to thee till death.
Faith of our moth-ers, guid - ing faith, We will be true to thee till death.
Faith of our moth-ers, Christian faith, We will be true to thee till death.

Benediction

168

W. H. S.

W. HINES SIMS

Grace, love, and peace a - bide now with you; Through

Je - sus Christ, our great Re - deem - er. A - MEN.

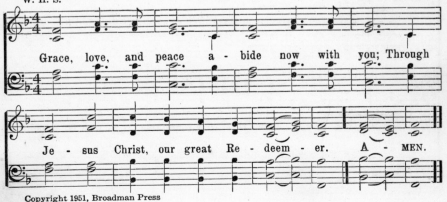

169 For All the Blessings of the Year

ALBERT H. HUTCHINSON

JOHN B. DYKES

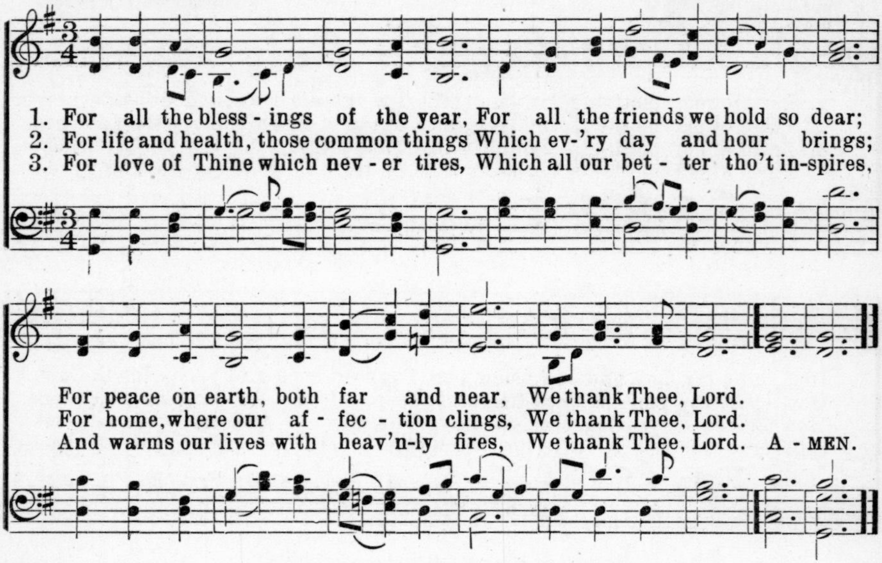

1. For all the bless - ings of the year, For all the friends we hold so dear;
2. For life and health, those common things Which ev - 'ry day and hour brings;
3. For love of Thine which nev - er tires, Which all our bet - ter tho't in-spires,

For peace on earth, both far and near, We thank Thee, Lord.
For home, where our af - fec - tion clings, We thank Thee, Lord.
And warms our lives with heav'n-ly fires, We thank Thee, Lord. A - MEN.

170 Welcome, New Juniors!

LILLIAN MOORE RICE

B. B. McKINNEY

Wel-come, wel-come, wel-come, hear us as we say: We are g-l-

a - d, glad, you have come to stay! We're hap - py thro' and thro' to

wel-come you and you Be-cause to-day your name is Jun - ior too!

Thou Art Near, O Lord

PSALM 119: 151
PSALM 136: 1

KATHERINE P. GOLDEN

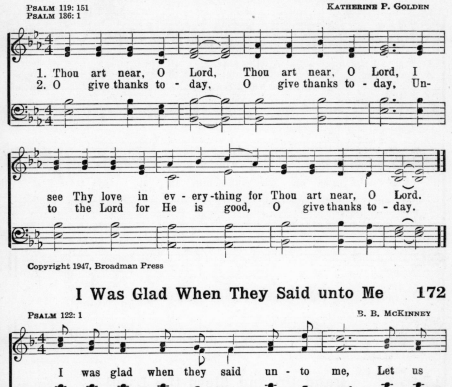

1. Thou art near, O Lord, Thou art near, O Lord, I
2. O give thanks to - day, O give thanks to - day, Un-

see Thy love in ev - ery - thing for Thou art near, O Lord.
to the Lord for He is good, O give thanks to - day.

I Was Glad When They Said unto Me   172

PSALM 122: 1

B. B. McKINNEY

I was glad when they said un - to me, Let us

go in - to the house of the Lord; I was glad when they said

un - to me, Let us go in - to the house of the Lord.

173   Trust in the Lord

PROVERBS 3: 5–6

ETHEL V. WILLIAMS

Trust in the Lord with all thine heart; and lean not un-
to thine own un-der-stand-ing. In all thy ways ac-
knowl-edge him, and he shall di-rect thy paths.

174   Stand Up and Bless the Lord!

NEHEMIAH 9: 5

ETHEL V. WILLIAMS

Stand up, stand up and bless the Lord your
God for-ev - er and ev - er.

Remember the Sabbath Day

175

Exodus 20: 8-11

ETHEL V. WILLIAMS

Re-mem-ber, re-mem-ber the sab-bath day, To keep it ho - ly.

Six days shalt thou la-bor, And do all thy work: But the sev-enth day Is the

sab-bath... The Lord blessed the sab - bath day, And hal - lowed it.

Be Strong

176

Ephesians 6: 10

ETHEL V. WILLIAMS

Be strong! Be strong! Be strong in the

Lord, and in the pow - er of his might.

The Hundredth Psalm

FAITH CHAMBERS WILSON

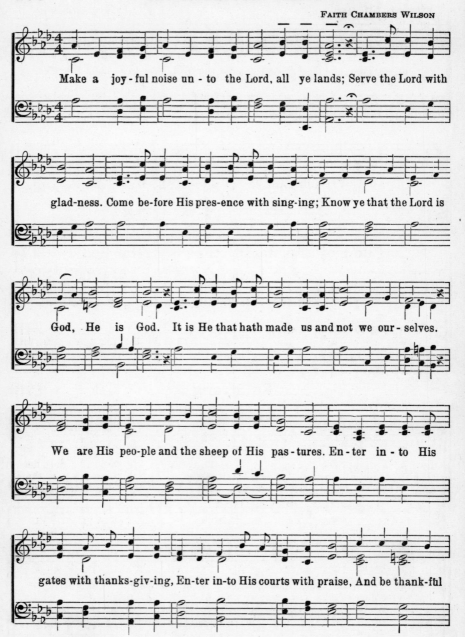

Make a joy-ful noise un-to the Lord, all ye lands; Serve the Lord with

glad-ness. Come be-fore His pres-ence with sing-ing; Know ye that the Lord is

God, He is God. It is He that hath made us and not we our-selves.

We are His peo-ple and the sheep of His pas-tures. En-ter in-to His

gates with thanks-giv-ing, En-ter in-to His courts with praise, And be thank-ful

The Hundredth Psalm

un - to Him, and bless His name; For the Lord is good, And His mer - cy

ev - er-last-ing, And His truth en - dur - eth to all gen - er - a - tions.

God of the Earth, the Sky, the Sea 178

SAMUEL LONGFELLOW

HENRY F. HEMY and J. G. WALTON

1. God of the earth, the sky, the sea! Mak-er of all a - bove, be - low!
2. Thy love is in the sun-shine's glow, Thy life is in the quick-'ning air;
3. We feel Thy calm at evening's hour, Thy gran-deur in the march of night;

Cre - a - tion lives and moves in Thee, Thy pres-ent life thro' all doth flow.
When lightnings flash and stormwinds blow, There is Thy pow'r; Thy law is there.
And, when Thy morn-ing breaks in pow'r, We hear Thy word, "Let there be light."

REFRAIN

We give Thee thanks, Thy name we sing, Al-might - y Fa-ther, heav'nly King.

179 Bring Thank Offerings

2 CHRONICLES 29: 31

ETHEL V. WILLIAMS

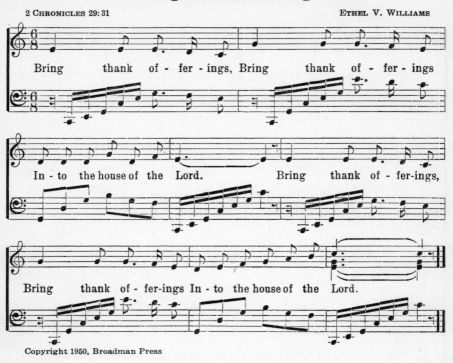

Bring thank of-fer-ings, Bring thank of-fer-ings
In-to the house of the Lord. Bring thank of-fer-ings,
Bring thank of-fer-ings In-to the house of the Lord.

180 We Give Thee But Thine Own

WILLIAM WALSHAM HOW

JOSEPH BARNBY

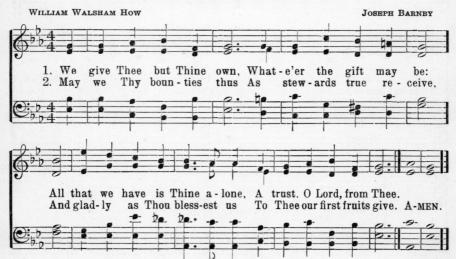

1. We give Thee but Thine own, What-e'er the gift may be:
2. May we Thy boun-ties thus As stew-ards true re-ceive,

All that we have is Thine a-lone, A trust. O Lord, from Thee.
And glad-ly as Thou bless-est us To Thee our first fruits give. A-MEN.

Tread Softly

FANNY J. CROSBY

W. H. DOANE

1. Be si - lent, be si - lent, A whis-per is heard, Be si - lent, and
2. Be si - lent, be si - lent, For ho - ly this place, This al - tar that
3. Be si - lent, be si - lent, His mer - cy re - cord, Be si - lent, be

CHORUS

lis - ten, O treas - ure each word! Tread soft - ly, tread soft - ly, The
ech - oes The mes-sage of grace. Tread soft - ly here, tread soft - ly here,
si - lent And wait on the Lord.

Mas - ter is here. Tread soft - ly, tread soft - ly, He bids us draw near.
Tread soft - ly here, tread soft - ly here,

TOPICAL INDEX

INDEX

Titles in CAPS and SMALL CAPS. First lines in lower case